LIFE SCIENCE LIBRARY

SHIPS

TIME
LIFE
BOOKS

LIFE SCIENCE LIBRARY

CONSULTING EDITORS
René Dubos
Henry Margenau
C. P. Snow

SHIPS

by Edward V. Lewis, Robert O'Brien
and the Editors of LIFE

TIME INCORPORATED, NEW YORK

ABOUT THIS BOOK

SHIPS have had a profound effect on civilization. Since prehistoric times man has used them to explore, to trade and to conquer. Control of the sea, in both commerce and war, has built great empires; loss of that control has often brought their destruction. Today, ships are as important as they have ever been. This book is largely devoted to the many ships of the present—their design, their construction and their employment. It sketches their evolution, and describes the expanding technology—based on such diverse disciplines as hydrodynamics, applied mathematics, metallurgy, electronics, nuclear physics, even aerodynamics—that in the past hundred years has helped to keep naval architecture in step with the rest of a fast-moving world.

Each text chapter is accompanied by a supplementary picture essay, though each may be read independently. For example, Chapter 1, "The Floating Box," tells of the design and construction of ships; it precedes a picture essay, "Ships on the Assembly Line," which describes in detail the building of a ship in one of the world's most up-to-date shipyards.

THE AUTHORS

EDWARD V. LEWIS is a research professor at Webb Institute of Naval Architecture, Glen Cove, Long Island. Formerly on the staff of a New York naval architectural firm, and of the Davidson Laboratory, Hoboken, New Jersey, Professor Lewis has written extensively on his specialty, ship behavior in waves.

ROBERT O'BRIEN, former newspaper columnist, was a senior staff writer for *Collier's* Magazine. He is the author of two previous volumes in the LIFE Science Library, *Machines* and *Weather*.

THE CONSULTING EDITORS

RENE DUBOS, member and professor of Rockefeller University, is a noted microbiologist and pathologist. He wrote *Mirage of Health* and *The Dreams of Reason* and is coauthor of *Health and Disease* in this series.

HENRY MARGENAU is Eugene Higgins Professor of Physics and Natural Philosophy at Yale, and an authority in spectroscopy and nuclear physics. He wrote *The Nature of Physical Reality* and is coauthor of *The Scientist* in this series.

C. P. SNOW has won an international audience for his novels, including *The New Men*, *The Affair* and *Corridors of Power*, which explore the effects of science on today's society. He was named to the British Ministry of Technology in 1964.

ON THE COVER

The sharp bow of the ocean liner S.S. *France* cuts through English Channel waters, its clean line interrupted by the 15-ton bow anchor. On the back cover, a stylized illustration of a marine propeller symbolizes the role of technology in the making of the modern ship.

Ships © 1965 Time Inc. All rights reserved.
Published simultaneously in Canada. Library of Congress catalogue card number 65-28742.
School and library distribution by Silver Burdett Company.

CONTENTS

TIME-LIFE BOOKS

EDITOR
Norman P. Ross

EXECUTIVE EDITOR
Maitland A. Edey

TEXT DIRECTOR ART DIRECTOR
Jerry Korn Edward A. Hamilton

CHIEF OF RESEARCH
Beatrice T. Dobie

Assistant Art Director: Arnold C. Holeywell
Assistant Chiefs of Research:
Monica O. Horne, Martha Turner

PUBLISHER
Rhett Austell

General Manager: Joseph C. Hazen Jr.
Planning Director: Frank M. White
Business Manager: John D. McSweeney
Circulation Manager: Joan D. Manley
Publishing Board: Nicholas Benton,
Louis Bronzo, James Wendell Forbes,
John S. Wiseman

LIFE MAGAZINE

EDITOR: Edward K. Thompson
MANAGING EDITOR: George P. Hunt
PUBLISHER: Jerome S. Hardy

LIFE SCIENCE LIBRARY

SERIES EDITOR: Martin Mann
Editorial staff for *Ships:*
Associate Editor: Robert G. Mason
Text Editors: James A. Maxwell, Harvey B. Loomis
Picture Editor: Robert W. Bone
Designer: Albert Sherman
Associate Designer: Edwin Taylor
Staff Writers: Timothy Carr, George Constable,
Leon Greene, Simon Johnson, Jonathan Kastner,
Peter Meyerson
Chief Researcher: Thelma C. Stevens
Researchers: Sarah Bennett, Edward Brash,
Valentin Y. L. Chu, Adrian G. Condon,
Leah Dunaief, Ann Ferebee, John Hochmann,
Alice Kantor, Anthony Wolff
EDITORIAL PRODUCTION
Color Director: Robert L. Young
Copy Staff: Marian Gordon Goldman,
Suzanne Seixas, Dolores A. Littles
Picture Bureau: Margaret K. Goldsmith,
Joan Lynch
Art Assistants: Douglas B. Graham,
Patricia Byrne, Charles Mikolaycak

The text for the chapters of this book was written by Edward V. Lewis and Robert O'Brien, for the picture essays by the editorial staff. The following individuals and departments of Time Incorporated were helpful in the production of the book: Henry Groskinsky and George Silk, LIFE staff photographers; Doris O'Neil, Chief of the LIFE Picture Library; Richard M. Clurman, Chief of the TIME-LIFE News Service; and Content Peckham, Chief of the Time Inc. Bureau of Editorial Reference.

INTRODUCTION

MOST OF THE MANY BOOKS written on the history of ships have been concerned with the romance of the sea, concentrating on the colorful period of sail or the drama of naval warfare. Significant as these aspects of the subject are, they should not overshadow the great importance of modern marine transportation. An operating merchant marine is essential to the national welfare. Again and again, events have shown that a high price must be paid for neglect of ships and shipping. The price is not merely economic; it involves foreign relations, military security and the essence of national power.

The role that ships and shipping fill in our society is recognized by the increasing attention being accorded them today. Once the creations of art and craftsmanship alone, ships are now among the most striking products of science and technology. The basic problems of hull design, propulsion and what might be called sea kindliness are being attacked with advanced mathematics and complexly instrumented model testing. New techniques of automation are converting shipyards, long the province of the individual artisan, into mass-production factories, and may remedy the inefficiencies of traditional cargo-handling techniques. Accelerating research into radical new forms of waterborne transportation suggests the possibility of new types of ships for the future.

Recognizing these facts, *Ships* is primarily concerned not with maritime art or seafaring history, but with the development of seagoing vessels over the ages. It conveys the drama of the progression from wooden ships and undependable sail to steel and steam, while providing a clear introduction to the elegant concepts of science underlying ship design.

—H. I. CHAPPELLE
Curator of Transportation
Museum of History and Technology
Smithsonian Institution

1
The
Floating
Box

A NEW GREAT LAKES ORE CARRIER TAKES TO THE WATERS OF THE DETROIT RIVER, HURTLING SIDEWAYS IN A LAUNCHING TECHNIQUE USED WHERE SPACE IS RESTRICTED.

A MODERN OCEANGOING SHIP is basically a floating steel box. But it is a box of almost unimaginable complexity, shaped and equipped by man to carry thousands of human lives at a time, or thousands of tons of cargo, across the widest oceans. It must be capable of withstanding the awesome forces of weather and the pounding of waves coming from a hundred different directions. It must combine strength and flexibility, great power and the precise balance to roll with the punches of the sea. A ship is a box that can be controlled by a small wheel and be guided across the trackless sea by stars and a few devices made by man.

Ships were not always so seaworthy, and learning to build them that way did not come easily. The modern ship evolved over the centuries from the hard-earned experiences of the men who sailed its predecessors, and from the bold experiments of intrepid pioneers. But it also came into being through the imagination and work of physicists and metallurgists, engineers and mathematicians, abstract theorists and practical architects, of electronic experts and brawny workmen.

The success of all this collaborative effort to build a sound ship is manifest to everyone who looks upon her. The Irish playwright Sean O'Casey, viewing the passenger liner which was to take him from England to the United States, wrote, "The whole aspect of her shouted to all who looked that she had a mighty confidence in herself, her broad sides and sturdy bow asking what wave on God's ocean could topple her over."

Man has good reason for wanting ships with this "mighty confidence." Ships have played vital roles in the affairs of the world, both in times of war and in times of peace. They have enabled man to explore, to colonize, to trade—and also to turn pirate, to blockade ports and to spread destruction. Ships have linked the peoples of the world, fed and clothed them, provided markets for their raw materials and handiwork. But invading armies have also been transported and supplied by ships, and warships have fought battles that have changed the course of history.

The variety of their uses is only one of the problems that confront the builders of ships. Everyone who designs a water vehicle—from a Sunday skipper drawing plans for a sailboat to be built in his garage, to a team of architects creating a giant ocean liner—must be certain that the vessel has three fundamental properties. These are buoyancy—the ability to float under all probable conditions; stability—the combination of proper dimensions and distribution of weight which will enable her to roll with the forces of wind and wave and always to return to the upright and even keel; and strength—structural soundness sufficient to support herself and all she contains no matter how rough the water becomes.

Obviously the purpose for which the craft will be used and the water in which she will operate dictate the degrees of buoyancy, stability and strength needed. An oceangoing ship that must face the fury of storms and pounding waves must be designed and built with qualities unnecessary for the towboat plying the placid rivers of the Mississippi Valley.

To design and build a vessel that is meant to face the unpredictable, often violent sea has been a concern of man since the dawn of history.

In Asia, Africa and Europe there were venturesome, imaginative men who looked upon the great oceans disappearing over the horizon and saw them not as barriers but as thoroughfares to new lands.

Men had to invent and then improve upon the craft that could use these thoroughfares, and for centuries experience was the only teacher. The knowledge was hard bought—acquired at the cost of ships capsizing, of foundering, of breaking apart in storms; acquired at the cost of uncounted thousands of human lives lost at sea. But knowledge was gained and passed on to following generations.

In the 19th Century, science and the scientific method made great strides and then, for the first time, the shipbuilder no longer had to rely solely on lessons handed down or empirically learned. Well-known physical principles could be applied to the problems of buoyancy, stability and strength while ships were still in the planning stage. Models of hulls could be tested in tanks to find what resistance a full-scale ship would offer to motion through the water. In the same century, technological advances made possible the building of larger, faster, more reliable ships than ever before: ships were now made of metal instead of wood; mechanical power replaced the sail.

A technological revolution solves many old problems, but it also creates new ones. Planning a modern powered ship involves consideration of a multitude of complex factors that never faced the designer of a sailing craft. Basically, however, there are the same three problems that faced the first man who fashioned a canoe from a log: the creation of a craft with buoyancy, stability and strength.

Finding a principle in a tub

It was Archimedes, musing in his bath one day in 250 B.C., who hit upon the principle of buoyancy: a body partially or completely immersed in a fluid is buoyed up, or sustained, by a force equal to the weight of the fluid displaced. Cork and wood float because they are less dense than water. Metal, however, is denser, and a one-pound chunk of bronze dropped into a tub of water will plummet to the bottom. But if this same pound of bronze is hammered into a thin, shallow bowl, it will float. Now it is presenting a considerably larger surface to the water, displacing a pound of it, and a force equal to the weight of the displaced water is buoying up the bowl.

Despite the ease with which Archimedes' principle could be proven, advocates of iron ships were still being derided as fools and dreamers in the late 18th and early 19th Centuries. "Wood can swim, iron can't," old tars said. But in 1787 John Wilkinson's 70-foot barge *Trial*, constructed of iron plates, did stay afloat, and in 1821 the 106-foot *Aaron Manby*, the first iron steamer, safely crossed the English Channel. Reluctantly, the

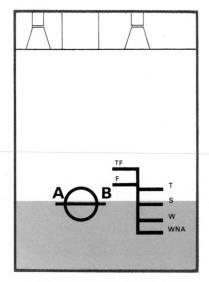

LOAD LINE MARKS on a hull show depths to which a ship can be legally loaded in various zones and seasons—tropical (T), summer (S) and winter (W)—and in fresh (F) and salt water. Due to bad winter weather in the North Atlantic, a ship headed there is less heavily laden (i.e., to line WNA). Letters "A" and "B" stand for The American Bureau of Shipping.

A FULLY LOADED TANKER has more of its hull underwater than above it. The depth the hull is permitted to settle *(shown in green)*— i.e., the vessel's displacement—is legally determined by load line marks placed on the hull amidships *(detail above)*. Figures called draft marks on the stern and bow *(above, right)* measure the hull's depth in the water.

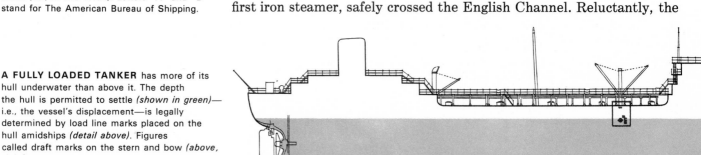

10

skeptics fell silent.

In time, applied mathematics removed all guesswork from figuring a vessel's buoyancy. Every modern ship has a formal displacement curve plotted by her architects from the lines and dimensions of her hull. This graph is turned over to her officers on her delivery. To gauge the ship's weight or displacement at any time during loading or unloading, they simply take the average of the bow and stern drafts—the vertical distances between the water line and the keel. A glance at the graph tells them, in tons, the amount of water she is displacing. The figure is, of course, the precise equivalent of her own weight plus everything aboard. Conversely, the officers can learn from the graph what her draft will be under any given load.

But merely being certain that a ship will float is not enough; it must have the ability to remain afloat under all probable conditions. Therefore, the hull of a modern steel vessel is compartmented by watertight, transverse divisions called bulkheads. If, through collision, shellfire or other circumstances, one section of the hull is flooded, the other compartments are designed to maintain sufficient buoyancy to keep the vessel from sinking. Highly compartmented ships, such as tankers, have even been sheared in two by collision, and the individual parts have remained afloat.

The rocking-chair tendency

Stability—the tendency of a ship rolling from side to side always to return to an upright position like a rocking chair or a weighted doll— is the second vital element which must be part of a vessel's design. Symmetry is an initial condition. The architect plans port and starboard sides of the hull as mirror images of each other. To know in advance the total weight of the ship and the exact distribution, designers tabulate everything that goes into the ship from the huge power plant to the crew's bunks.

There are two forces, operating in opposite directions, which affect the stability of every ship. One is the summation of the entire weight of the ship—the downward force acting at the center of gravity. The other is the supporting force of the water, which acts upward through the center of buoyancy. When a ship is at anchor in a placid harbor (as shown on page 12), its center of gravity is located directly above its center of buoyancy on the vertical center line of the vessel.

However, if a wave from a passing vessel causes her to heel momentarily (shown bottom, page 12), this positioning changes. If the tilt is to starboard, for example, the center of buoyancy is transferred laterally to the right. The relationship between the centers of buoyancy and gravity now becomes vital. If the center of gravity is sufficiently low, it will be

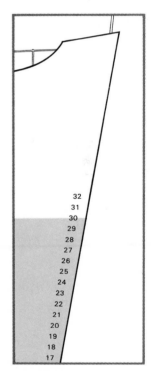

DRAFT MARKS on a vessel's bow measure the distance in feet from the ship's keel to its waterline *(arrow)*. Similar marks on the stern show the depth aft; ship's draft is the average of bow and stern drafts. Maritime law requires that the figures be six inches high and spaced six inches apart. The ship illustrated here shows a forward draft of 30'2".

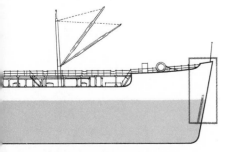

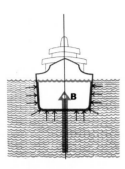

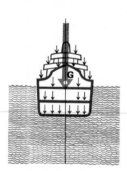

BUOYANCY AND GRAVITY are the two forces acting on a ship as it floats at rest. The water pushes all around on the submerged hull *(small arrows, above)*. The total push acts as a single upward buoyant force, B, exerted at the center of the submerged part of the hull. The downward force of gravity is equal to the weight of the ship and everything in it *(small arrows, below)*. The total force, G, is exerted at approximately the center of the ship.

to the left of the center of buoyancy, and the downward force of gravity and the upward force of buoyancy combine to push the vessel back to an upright position. However, if the center of gravity is too high (as shown on page 13), it will be to the right of the center of buoyancy. Now the downward and upward forces are combined to aggravate the heel and the ship may capsize.

About the mid-18th Century, Pierre Bouguer, a French mathematician and a founder of modern naval architecture, worked out a practical means, still in standard use, for evaluating the stability of a ship. Bouguer's concept was based on a point he called the metacenter, located at the intersection of the center line of the hull and a vertical line through the center of buoyancy of a listing ship. The distance between the metacenter, M, and the center of gravity, G, Bouguer proved, would measure a ship's stability. This distance, usually referred to as GM, is a matter of prime concern to the designer. If G is above M, there is danger of capsizing. If the GM is small, i.e., the center of gravity is below, but still too close to M, the ship will make long, slow rolls and may readily capsize in the event of a collision. However, if G is too far below M, the vessel will be "stiff" and jerk back to the upright, possibly damaging the cargo and injuring the crew and passengers. A safe GM for the average fully loaded merchant ship is about 5 per cent of her beam—the breadth at her widest part.

The center of gravity is dependent upon distribution of weight in the ship and therefore shifts with each addition or unloading of cargo, with each fueling and with each hour's consumption of fuel at sea. It is the job of the ship's architect to take all such factors into consideration, to calculate the position of M and then forecast the vessel's GM value under all foreseeable situations and conditions.

Dock tests for calculations

However, before a ship goes to sea, she is put through an actual test to verify her calculated stability. First, tracks are installed across the ship's deck. A jumbo truck carrying several tons of weight is then put on the tracks and rolled to one side of the ship or the other, thus causing the vessel to list. At various positions of the truck from the center line of the ship, the designer measures the angle of inclination of the heeling ship by means of hanging pendulum bobs. A trigonometric equation gives him the result he seeks: confirmation of the architect's estimated value of GM and hence the precise location of G. With this information, the GM from minimum to maximum load conditions can be calculated. These data are given to the ship's officers for their guidance at sea.

In addition to buoyancy and stability, the designer of a ship must give her the pliant strength that will enable her to absorb and with-

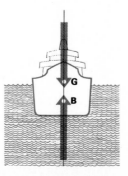

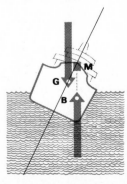

A STABLE SHIP is one that can right itself if it is heeled over. When it is upright, the ship's centers of gravity, G, and buoyancy, B, are in line. When the vessel is tilted, B moves in the direction of the slope so that its upward push combines with G's downward force to right the ship. This stability is measured by the position of the metacenter, M, a theoretical point where the upward force B meets the ship's vertical midline. The position of M above G here indicates good stability.

stand a combination of mighty forces—the upward force of buoyancy, the downward force of gravity, the powerful onslaught of ocean waves.

For thousands of years until the coming of the metal ship, the classic design of vessels was based on the vertebrate form. The keel was the spine to which wooden ribs were attached. This skeleton was then covered with a skin of hide, bark or planks. The skin not only gave the craft buoyancy but, together with the skeleton, provided the necessary strength to the hull.

But the time came when man needed longer, bigger ships, and no tree grew tall enough to provide single planks, or strakes, that would reach from stem to stern. Strakes had to be fashioned from two or more planks joined end to end. However, wherever one plank met another there was a weakness.

A solution in steel

The answer emerged from the Industrial Revolution: hulls built of metal; first iron and then steel. Metal plates could be stoutly riveted together, and when stiffened with metal frames and beams, a hull could be built that had the strength and resilience of a bridge.

The stiffened steel plates of a hull serve several purposes: they keep out the water and support the decks and the weight of everything on them. The total weight of the ship and its contents is borne by the bottom of the hull, which serves as the foundation for the vessel, just as footings do for a building.

The hull, in turn, receives its support from the buoyancy of the water beneath the ship. However, the forces of buoyancy are ever changing as waves pass along the length of the vessel. When the crests are at the bow and stern, the hull sags between them like a steel beam suspended between trestles; it therefore must be designed to bend without breaking. When a wave crest is amidships, the ship is in a "hogging" position; it bends the other way as if balanced on a fulcrum. Again the hull must have the strength and flexibility to withstand the bending load.

Although a new era began with the coming of the metal ship, two important holdovers from earlier days remain. One is a complicated system of tonnage measurements; the other is the arrangement of circle-and-gridlike markings at midships which show how much water the craft may safely draw under given conditions.

The basis of modern tonnage measurement for volume began in the 13th Century, when merchant ships carried large cargoes of wine in giant casks which were called tuns. Hence, the number of tuns a ship could carry was a rough gauge of her capacity. By the 15th Century, England had established standards for the wine-filled tun: capacity, 250 gallons; volume, about 57 cubic feet; weight, 2,240 pounds. In the 17th

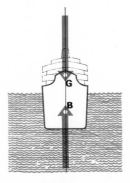

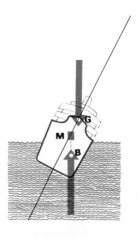

AN UNSTABLE SHIP cannot return to a normal upright position when tilted. Since the vessel is more narrow and top-heavy than a stable ship, B and G are located much farther apart *(arrows, left)*. When the vessel tilts, the force of G shifts toward the direction of the slope; together the two opposing forces act to heel the ship even farther until it capsizes. The metacenter M, instead of being above G as in a stable ship *(opposite page)*, is here well below it.

Century—long after wine had ceased to be a major cargo—usage brought about the modern spellings, "ton" and "tonnage." The 2,240-pound ton —sometimes called the long ton—was retained for weight measurement. As a new means of measuring a ship's carrying space and her total volume, a space ton of 100 cubic feet was adopted in the 19th Century.

Over the years, the measurements became increasingly complex. Although the subject bristles with technicalities and exceptions, tonnage figures today generally describe the vessel's interior volume, or her own weight calculated from the weight of the water she displaces. Displacement tonnage usually refers to the weight of the ship at its normal full load. Deadweight tonnage is the designation of the number of tons a vessel may carry in cargo, stores, water, fuel, passengers and crew. Gross tonnage is a measure of volume in units of 100 cubic feet of a ship's total closed-in space minus certain exempted areas such as ballast tanks and galleys. Net tonnage is gross tonnage minus space allotted for machinery, engine room, officers' and crew's quarters and similar uses. Approximate values for a typical modern cargo vessel 525 feet long would be: 21,000 tons displacement; 13,500 tons deadweight; 9,200 gross tons; 5,400 net tons. In general, passenger liners are described in terms of gross tonnage; naval ships in displacement tons; freighters and tankers in deadweight tons.

Safety marks on the hull

Also from the past are the painted lines, called Plimsoll marks, visible on the side of a ship to indicate minimum freeboard, i.e., the minimum allowable distance between the water line and the top of the hull. Samuel Plimsoll, a member of the British Parliament from 1868 to 1880, was concerned about the loss of ships at sea because of overloading, and he devised a simple circle bisected horizontally by a straight bar *(page 10)* as a means of telling a port officer immediately if a vessel had more cargo aboard than she was authorized to carry. The letters on the Plimsoll disk designate the assigning authority: on U.S. ships, for example, they are "AB" for American Bureau of Shipping; on British vessels "LR" for Lloyd's Register; on French ships "BV" for Bureau Veritas.

Since Plimsoll's time, other load lines have been added. Just forward of the Plimsoll disk on freighters and tankers are one vertical and six extending horizontal lines, which indicate the authorized load limits for various zones and sea conditions. There are also two series of numbers at bow and stern. These show the draft—the distance in feet or meters between the water line and keel.

The space tonnage of a ship, the weight she will be able to carry, her draft under given loads and the amount of freeboard she must have for different zones and sea conditions are all accurately calculated by the

UPPER DECK (TOP VIEW)

THE GROSS TONNAGE of a ship represents its total internal space *(green, below)*. It is a measure of volume, not weight, taken in units of 100 cubic feet. Thus, a ship of 7,000 gross tons has 700,000 cubic feet of internal space. This includes areas inside closed structures on the upper deck *(green, above)*, and space occupied by the machinery *(dark gray)*. It does not include areas such as the galley, lavatories and parts of the superstructure.

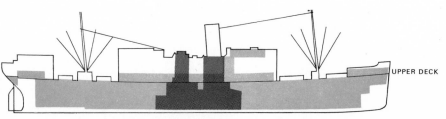

UPPER DECK

GROSS TONNAGE

ship's architects while they are designing the vessel.

As the plans are finished and approved, there comes the enormous task of translating them into steel, aluminum, plastics and a hundred other materials. The drawings first go to the shipyard's mold loft. Here, in one of several ways, depending on the techniques of the yard, they are converted into patterns for the actual metalwork. The drawings may be transformed into full-sized wooden templates that are to the shipbuilder what tissue-paper sleeve, skirt and bodice patterns are to the dressmaker: they outline the final components—the steel plates for decks and bulkheads, for sides and bottom and for the myriad other structural members of the ship. Or, the plans may be duplicated on glass slides, and projected full-sized by light upon the steel plate. Workmen then trace the outlines in chalk or paint for the cutting torches to follow. Or 1/100-scale templates may be made to provide controls for electronically operated cutting torches.

Tailoring the steel

Next, in the heat and clamor of the structural and anglesmith shops, a thousand skilled metal craftsmen cut the hull and deck plates, cut and shape the curving transverse frames that strengthen the ship crosswise, the slender beams that stiffen her decks and bulkheads, the pillars and stanchions that sustain the beams.

The made-to-order parts, some of them pierced with cutouts to reduce weight, now travel to nearby assembly areas. Shipfitters deftly put the components in place. Welders, faceless in their robotlike masks, stitch them together with the white-hot blaze of electric arcs into whole sections of side shell, cellular double bottom, deck plating. Now the tall overhead cranes pick up 70- and 150-ton subassemblies as big as houses, swing them through the air and delicately lower them into position in the building berth. Gradually, the ship begins to materialize. The great steel box grows longer, acquires a high bow, rounded stern, propellers, thin blade of rudder.

Some yards build ships in dry docks below sea level. When the hull and superstructure are finished, yard workers open valves. The water floods in and the ship is gently floated off her shores and keel blocks. Other yards on the Great Lakes and on inland waterways launch ships sideways. But most builders slide her sternfirst into her natural element.

A few weeks before launching, shipwrights fashion the cradle that will keep her upright as she goes to meet the water. Carefully they lay down an inch-thick layer of launching grease between the ground ways and the cradle that will be removed once she is afloat. (Builders sometimes use other lubricating agents: more than one ship has slipped down her ways on a layer of bananas.)

UPPER DECK (TOP VIEW)

THE NET TONNAGE of a vessel is, like its gross tonnage *(diagrams opposite)*, a measure of volume. But it is a better index of a ship's earning power since it represents roughly passenger and cargo spaces *(green, above and below)*. It is found by subtracting part of the machinery space *(gray, below)* and other "nonearning" areas, such as those for the crew, from the gross tonnage. Mooring and harbor fees are based on the net tonnage.

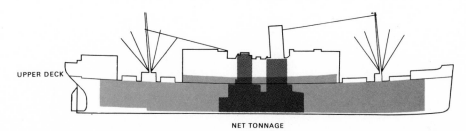

UPPER DECK

NET TONNAGE

But the ship usually is far from finished when it is launched. There follow months at the outfitting pier for installation of her power plant and furnishings—comfortable officers' and crew's quarters, and perhaps a half-dozen functionally appointed staterooms if she is a cargo ship or tanker; or an entire community of suites, bedrooms, theaters, restaurants, swimming pools, bars and shops if she is a passenger ship.

And here, finally, she receives the circulation and nerve systems that bring her to life: pumps and pipes for conveying fresh and salt water and steam heat, for shifting fuel oil from double-bottom tanks to fire-room settling tanks, for clearing leakage and drainage water; battalions of fans and mazes of ducts to supply warm or cold air to staterooms, galleys and crew's quarters, to dehumidify cargo spaces, to deliver refreshing blasts of cool air below decks to engine room and machinery space; humming generators and a thousand miles of wires and cable for making and conducting the electricity that lights the ship and powers her various equipment.

Once they are in, once she has steamed back from her sea trials with a broom lashed to her masthead to signify a clean sweep of her speed, maneuvering and other tests, she is accepted as a member of the world's ocean fleet. Now she is self-contained, self-sufficient in the world of sea and sky for which she was designed.

Ships on the Assembly Line

Over the centuries, not only ships but the methods of building them have changed radically. Nowhere is this more apparent today than at the Arendal shipyard near the Swedish port of Göteborg. Here, on a site where the Vikings might have hand-crafted their sturdy "long ships" a thousand years ago, a new breed of shipbuilders turns out vessels in what is actually a highly mechanized ship factory. Arendal combines the assembly-line principle with the prefabrication process devised by American yards during World War II to build fleets of Liberty and Victory ships. By adopting the best shipbuilding techniques used in other modern yards and combining them with innovations of its own, Arendal has devised a unique production line that can turn out a 70,000-ton (deadweight) tanker in 18 weeks—about half the time required by older yards. And even as one ship is being finished, workers have begun putting together the next *(right)*.

A PREFABRICATED STERN
In a shower of sparks, an Arendal worker grinds smooth the edges of plates that form the rigid skeleton of a section that will be part of a tanker's stern. This operation assures a perfect weld when the vessel's steel skin is attached to the ribbed framework. Dozens of such prefabricated sections, some of them weighing as much as 300 tons, eventually will be assembled to construct the hull.

One 780-foot vessel nears completion in one of Arendal's building docks as another *(right)* emerges from the assembly shop. To launch a

From Plate Yard to Building Dock

The two ships at left, emerging stern first from a huge assembly shop, represent the end of a production line that is almost a mile long.

It begins at top center, in the plate yard where the steel to be used for the ships arrives at the yard. In many shipyards as much as 75 per cent of steel handling involves merely moving the plates from one operation to the next. At Arendal, there is no waste motion: each plate moves on the production line in a straight line from step to step. After being cleaned, shaped and welded into basic components in various buildings en route, the plates arrive at the assembly shop, where the ship is put together. There is no keel-laying since the hull is built in sections, complete with bulkheads, machinery and even piping. As each segment is added on, the hull is pushed by powerful hydraulic pistons out into one of two building docks. There cranes add engines and superstructure. This production system can produce as many as six 70,000-ton ships every year.

SHIPBUILDING'S HENRY FORD
Nils Svensson, Managing Director of Götaverken, the Swedish shipbuilding firm that owns Arendal, displays the original Arendal model, built in his basement in 1957. Svensson pioneered the adaptation of automobile assembly-line techniques to the shipbuilding process.

finished ship, the dock is flooded through lock gates, out of sight at the bottom of the picture.

Putting a Ship on Paper

Speed, planning and uniformity are the keys to Arendal's efficient production system. To simplify operations, the yard accepts orders only for oil tankers and bulk carriers, preferably in series of identical design, leaving the less standardized passenger liners and warships to other yards. Before a single machine goes into action, the movement of every component of a ship, from the first plate to the last can of paint, is precisely plotted. It takes 70,000 man-hours simply to draw up the stacks of plans needed for a new design.

From this pile of detailed work plans come the instructions that start heavy slabs of steel rolling through automatic straightening, cleaning and paint-spraying machinery. Next the metal travels to the plate shop, where each plate is marked with the coded symbols indicating that it is to be cut, bent or welded. Now the steel is ready to be fashioned into the components that will ultimately become a ship.

A PILE OF PLANS
Checking specifications against plans, draftsmen make drawings for some of the 600 sets of blueprints needed for building one ship—which will have only a number till it is launched. A wooden scale model in front of the window is marked with the location of all external plates.

A SPRAY OF PROTECTION
Brilliant primer paint, squirting from automatic sprayers, rust-proofs both sides of a shining plate after it has been straightened and cleaned. Many man-hours are saved by applying the primer at this time instead of when the hull is completed, as in the usual shipyard practice.

MOVING PLATES BY PUSH BUTTON

Supervised by the plate-shop boss, who has push-button control over the steel that flows through the shop, a magnetic crane descends to pick up plates, temporarily identified by color-coded panels like those on the sill. The television monitor shows plates on their way to the shop.

A CODE FOR STEELWORK

Each plate is carefully marked, according to a master numbering plan, before being fed to the plate shop's cutting and bending machines. The large size of the plates—some measure 9 x 46 feet—reduces the amount of time-consuming joining and welding work in each hull section.

Slicing Metal
by Remote Control

The most dramatic example of modern technology at Arendal occurs in the plate shop, where robotlike gas torches cut the great steel plates to shape. No human hand guides the blazing jets as they slice unerringly into the steel amid showers of orange sparks, cutting intricate patterns in the metal. The old hand-cutting technique requires workmen to follow lines that have been traced on each plate from a full-sized wooden template; it is a slow and often inexact process. The mechanized torches of Arendal, linked to the movement of an electronic control unit in a nearby command center, can rapidly cut four plates at a time to identical shapes.

AN ELECTRIC-EYE VIEW OF STEEL
Slicing through half-inch steel at 20 inches a minute, the 3,000° F. flame of an oxygen torch *(above)* follows a path dictated by the photoelectric apparatus in the booth shown at right. There, while a workman keeps watch, the image of a scale drawing is projected on a viewing table at one tenth full size. An electric-eye tracer moves over the table, following the plan's lighted white lines and guiding the progress of the cutting torches, which can be seen outside. The control booth is kept dark so that outside light will not affect the unit's photoelectric cell.

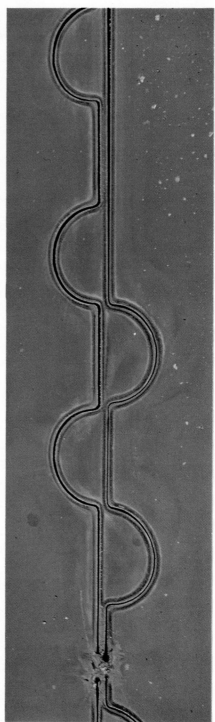

A PATTERN TRACED BY FLAME
The intricate curves cut into this steel plate illustrate the precision of the photoelectrically controlled torches. The cut is only one eighth of an inch wide; the discoloration on either side is caused by heat. When the plate is broken apart, the new pieces will have scalloped edges.

PRESSING CURVES INTO STEEL

Forcing complex curves into a suspended steel plate, a hydraulic press exerts up to 700 tons of force against a strategically placed metal block. Using variously shaped blocks—and a well-trained eye—the press operator is able to concentrate the force of his machine on small areas of the plate to produce just the right curve or angle prescribed by the work plans.

Rounding Out a Hull

In the interests of speed and simplicity, Arendal designers produce ships with as many flat surfaces as possible. About three quarters of the 4,600 plates that go into a 70,000-ton Arendal tanker are flat, which permits them to be swiftly processed on the assembly line. But every ship must have some curved plates, especially in the bow and stern. These pose a production problem that defies practicable solution by automation: each sheet of steel must be separately shaped into specified curves and angles. The shaping is done by heavy presses operated with delicate precision by skilled metal workers whose art is almost unchanged since steel replaced oak on the high seas.

USING WOOD TO MEASURE METAL

Employing an ancient technique to check his performance, a hydraulic-press operator holds a wooden template against a curved steel plate and looks for telltale glimpses of light that indicate an imperfect fit between wood and metal. This use of templates, built to match the exact curves called for in the plans, is one of the few traditional techniques still used at Arendal.

SHAPING A PLATE

With one swipe, a machine called a bending roll folds a right angle into a one-and-one-half-inch plate as though it were a sheet of tin. The plate is placed over a groove into which the bending roll descends, its 2,000 tons of force applied by a system of hydraulic jacks, gears and screws. This press can also bend a plate's edge to make a flange, or raised rim.

WELDING RIBS OF STEEL

The skeleton of a tanker's stern section is welded into shape as the processed plates arrive in the assembly shop. This section will be the bottom of a ballast tank and the semicircular holes, cut by torches in the plate shop, are for drainage of the tank's compartments. All welding at Arendal is done indoors to lessen the danger of the molten metal cracking as it cools.

JOINING THE HULL

Deftly maneuvered by two of the shop's eight overhead cranes, a 90-ton stern section is made ready to join the hull which has already been started in the building dock. Three work levels in the 33-foot-deep dock provide access for the addition of piping and other equipment.

THE SKIN OF A SHIP

The steel plates that form the skin of a prefabricated hull section are carefully lowered and aligned before being welded to the upside-down framework and to each other. Welding has replaced the older technique of riveting: the completed hull will be almost perfectly smooth.

Putting the Pieces Together

Arendal's huge assembly shop is a noisy, brightly lit building one seventh of a mile long and 100 feet high. Here, protected from capricious Swedish weather, workers fashion the sections that will be joined together to form the hull of a ship.

Some sections are built upside-down because the curve of the hull makes the frames and plates more accessible in that position. Then teams of overhead cranes lift the completed sections, gently right them, and lower them into the dry dock which extends into the building. The ship, resting on level ways, is built stern-first and is slowly pushed outside by five hydraulic pistons as each new 50-foot hull unit is added. Twenty motors close a complex of sliding, folding and rising doors to make a weathertight fit around the protruding hull. Outside, crews using 200-foot-high traveling cranes begin adding engines and superstructure—while inside, workers go on adding new sections to the hull.

Framed by the giant doors of the assembly shop, a completed vessel, still hung with scaffolding, waits for painting before being floated from

its building dock. A sister ship at right is nearing completion, while in the foreground the stern of the next ship is just beginning to take shape.

2
Designs to Tame the Sea

A DIORAMA OF DONALD McKAY'S FAMOUS BOSTON SHIPYARD IN 1851 SHOWS THREE CLIPPER SHIPS ON THE WAYS—"STAFFORDSHIRE," "FLYING CLOUD" AND "FLYING FISH."

EVERY SHIP, from sleek passenger liner to prosaic freighter, undergoes a startling transformation when she leaves port and heads for the open sea. At dockside she may have seemed clumsy and incongruous, like a tethered whale or a floating hotel. Now, in her natural element, she has suddenly acquired grace, beauty and life.

This change is neither a romantic notion nor a happy accident. Enormous effort, imagination and engineering skill have gone into building a vessel as nearly perfect as possible for the specific task of journeying across thousands of miles of trackless ocean, encountering all sorts of winds and seas. In few things made by man is design more completely determined by purpose, more ideally suited to self-sufficiency in a hostile environment.

First, the designer painstakingly planned the shaping of the hull to move through water with a minimum of power-wasting disturbance. Then there was the accurate calculation of the amount of power and the design of a screw to produce the desired speed. Thousands of man-hours of practical experience, engineering and scientific research and—perhaps most important of all—meticulous testing of ship models were combined to produce this remarkable and functional unity of hull form, propeller design and power plant. In the long history of shipbuilding, scientific model-testing is a comparatively recent development. For centuries, shipwrights built their vessels by a combination of intuition and hand-me-down rules of thumb. Precision was of no great concern. A buyer who specified a ship with a beam of 31 feet might find, on delivery, that it measured 33 feet. What difference, the shipwright would ask, did a foot or two matter on the high seas?

This rough-and-ready approach to dimensions had ceased to be tolerable when iron and steel hulls started to replace wooden ones in the middle of the 19th Century and steam engines were taking over from sails. These developments produced a whole new set of problems. Now there was propulsion, as well as the hull, to be considered. How much horsepower was needed to drive a given hull at a given speed?

There was no way of knowing exactly in advance. To be sure, theories existed, but they could not be tested, as the case of the notorious *Great Eastern* demonstrates. The *Great Eastern* was the most interesting and ambitious construction project of her day. She was a huge iron ocean liner, built back in the 1850s. She had paddle wheels, propellers *and* sails. She was almost as long as the great transatlantic giants of today; in fact, for 40 years she remained the largest ship of any kind ever built anywhere. Since nothing like her had ever been attempted before, her designer had to rely heavily on theory. All sorts of innovations in construction, design and power plant went into this vessel, but it was not until she was launched and tested that there was any way of telling how theory related to fact.

As it turned out, the *Great Eastern* had one fatal flaw: her hull was mismatched with her power plant. The coal she burned could not be paid for by the revenues she earned.

The first man to persevere in a scientific approach to the problems of hull design was an English engineer named William Froude. Froude had been connected with the development of British railroads and had also designed a set of bilge keels for the *Great Eastern* to reduce rolling. His experiences in the latter project brought him face to face with the fact that there should be a more rigorous method of evaluating hull performance. Testing full-sized vessels after they were built was impractical in his view, so he decided to test small-scale models.

Model ships in a model sea

This may seem like a ridiculously obvious idea today, but it was not then. Over the years men had occasionally tried to improve boats by towing models in streams and ponds, but their findings had produced no accurate way to "scale up" the observed action of a model to that of a full-sized hull. But now the desperate need for precise knowledge coincided with the flowering of the scientific method. Men like Froude were beginning to be able to apply comparatively new and effective techniques for attacking complex problems. They had learned to separate big and puzzling phenomena into simpler, independent components, and then to measure each component under rigidly controlled conditions.

Froude is said to have started by towing crude models in a sheltered creek. He learned enough to convince the British Admiralty to grant him £2,000 for more elaborate studies. He used the money to build a narrow test tank nearly 300 feet long with an overhead railroad track running from one end to the other. To this track he fitted a small carriage whose speed could be precisely regulated by a steam-powered winch. With his carriage, he could tow accurate models in still water at any desired speed, and make careful note of their behavior. A spring balance—like the old-fashioned scales once used to weigh ice and vegetables—was connected to the model, measuring the pull needed to keep it moving and thus indicating the total resistance which had to be overcome. Froude hoped to relate, by some simple mathematical formula, his measurements of the model's resistance to the resistance of a full-sized hull of similar shape. Then he would know how big an engine to specify for a ship—before the ship was built. And he could try different designs to find the most efficient shape without actually constructing anything bigger than a toy.

One source of resistance known to Froude was the waves made by the ship. Anyone who has watched a motorboat get under way in smooth water will have noticed that as the boat starts up, small waves form at bow and stern, and that these get bigger as the boat gathers speed. They result from the movement of water away from the boat and then back into place behind it; the energy expended in the creation of these waves

A 16TH CENTURY SHIPWRIGHT lays out a plan with a compass as an apprentice looks on. The drawing is in a manuscript of about 1586 called *Fragments of Ancient English Shipwrightry,* attributed to Matthew Baker, the first Englishman to put ship designs on paper. Earlier in the century, ship construction had been greatly stimulated by Henry VIII, who not only subsidized his own shipwrights but even imported Italian shipbuilders.

is known as wave-making resistance.

Froude's towing tank confirmed his previous observations about the waves. When a model moved slowly it made many small ripples; when it moved fast it made larger but fewer waves. But Froude discovered something new when he tested a series of models, each of exactly the same proportions but of different sizes. If towed at the same speed, they all made different wave patterns. But when a large model was speeded up, it would soon reach a velocity at which its wave pattern exactly matched the pattern created by a slower-moving small model. For hulls of the same shape, there seemed to be a connection between speed, size and wave pattern—and therefore between speed, size and wave-making resistance. What this relationship was Froude could only establish crudely, for his scale could not measure wave resistance alone, but only total resistance.

Now Froude made an intellectual jump. Another long-recognized source of resistance was friction—the retarding effect of molecules of water brushing against the hull. If friction were the only other major component of total resistance, then measuring it separately would give the wave resistance by simple subtraction. Only then could there be a chance of finding scaling factors to relate model measurements accurately to full-sized characteristics.

Underwater testing planks

To measure frictional resistance independently of wave resistance, Froude abandoned model hulls for a time and used sharp-edged planks, towing them completely submerged so that they made no waves at all. He again conducted several carefully planned series of tests, using planks of various lengths and various surface coatings—smooth varnish, cotton, sand, paraffin. It soon became apparent that both length and surface quality influenced frictional resistance, and after some arduous calculations, he derived a way of determining the frictional resistance of any plank (or hull) provided he knew its length, its surface area, the quality of that surface and the speed at which it was moving. Now he was on his way to breaking the problem wide open. By subtracting frictional resistance from total resistance of his various models, he was at last able to obtain wave-making resistance. From this he was free to go on to his next step: applying this knowledge to full-sized ships, which meant scaling up resistance according to a formula. Eventually he arrived at one. It turned out to be fairly simple: for hulls of the same shape, resistance is directly proportional to displacement at speeds where the wave patterns are similar.

There remained only the problem of testing the formulas against a real ship. He made an exact model of an existing seagoing vessel,

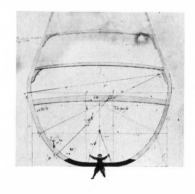

PLANS FOR A GALLEON are attributed to Matthew Baker, master shipwright to Queen Elizabeth in the 16th Century. Above is a cross section of the vessel at its widest point, called the midship bend. (The small figure of a man holding a compass indicates scale.) The superb draftsman skillfully drew lines and arcs to indicate the precise curvature of the hull. Below is one of his galleons in side view. The fish drawn beneath its water line reflects the traditional practice of giving a ship's underwater section the blunt head of a cod and tapering it toward the stern like the tail of a mackerel.

the *Greyhound*, calculated the wave-making and frictional resistance separately, scaled up his figures to the full-sized ship, and then predicted what the *Greyhound*'s resistance would be when towed at various speeds in quiet water. In due course, the test was made. Afterwards, Froude compared the results with calculations derived from the experiments with the model, and found that, by making a reasonable adjustment for the roughness of the *Greyhound*'s hull, his forecast was accurate. Ever since, model-testing has been accepted as a way of determining in advance the performance of an actual vessel. This technique is now generally regarded as one of the greatest advances ever made in shipbuilding.

Wind, waves and schedules

Froude also gave a great deal of thought to the nature of waves themselves, and made many studies of rolling, for he was aware that the introduction of power to seagoing vessels presented problems that had not been encountered before. A wind-driven ship is steadied against rolling by her sails, and since she is unable to sail directly into the wind, she seldom has to push directly into the waves. In the past she usually ran with the wind or across it—and the waves, rolling up from astern or from the side in an easy motion, presented little problem. Now, with steam, a ship could go in any direction she wished—even plowing directly into wind and waves. And with expanding trade and keen international transport competition, the time required for a voyage became more and more important. Today, a ship must be able to do more than log a certain speed under good weather conditions. As nearly as possible, she must be able to maintain her schedule in all seasons, in all states of sea.

At-sea operating costs for a modern high-speed cargo liner run as high as $5,000 a day. The oil she burns in a few minutes would heat a 12-room house in New England for an entire year. Even more expensive is the cost of handling cargo in port. If a ship arrives a day late, her company may have to pay out thousands of extra dollars in overtime to longshoremen to allow her to meet her next scheduled sailing date. At such penalty rates, it behooves a master to bring his ship in on time, if he can possibly do so in safety. Unfortunately seas are not always cooperative.

Rough seas retard a modern powered ship's progress in one of two ways, or in a combination of both. Not only must she battle the heightened resistance of wind and water but she must also cope with her own greatly increased pitching and rolling.

Planes can fly around or over heavy weather. Submarines (in the lingo of their crews) "fly" under it. But modern, high-powered passenger and cargo liners must take the weather as it comes and strive to meet their schedules. Even a well-designed ship may not be able to do this. Moving

A STUDY OF SHIPS' WAVES by the British engineer William Froude used models *(above)* to predict the performance of full-sized vessels. Froude sought to isolate a hull's wave-making resistance from the total resistance it meets while traveling through the water. Among other significant findings, he discovered that a small hull moving slowly makes proportionally the same wave pattern as a large hull moving faster *(below)*.

18-FOOT HULL, 9 KNOTS

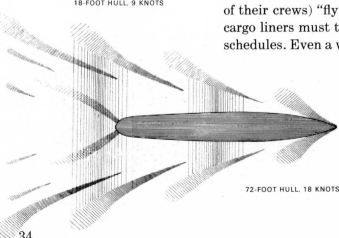

72-FOOT HULL, 18 KNOTS

34

at full speed in heavy beam seas she may develop such serious rolling that the captain is forced to head her into the wind to ease the violent swinging. Then she may begin to pitch, slam and ship water until he orders the chief engineer to cut back on the power.

The improvement of heavy-sea performance has been, and is, the objective of much research. Any study of ships in storms must obviously start with a study of waves. Mariners have been contending with waves for thousands of years, but it is only during the last 30 years that oceanographers have really learned much about them beyond the hard-earned empirical knowledge of the damage they can do—and beyond making estimates of their size.

Waves are made by wind. A breeze starts up, blows across calm water. Its frictional drag creates ripples. The breeze pushes against the sloping surface of the ripples and whips them into wavelets. Under the cumulative pressure of the wind, they grow as they advance. How big they will grow depends on the strength of the wind and on the amount of unobstructed open water there is for them to travel across. In a harbor only a few hundred yards wide, or in a small pond, really large waves will never build up no matter how hard the wind blows. But in the open sea, with an unobstructed "fetch" of a hundred miles or more, a fresh breeze will gradually build waves 10 or more feet high. Storms will create waves 50 or more feet high, and a U.S. Navy vessel once encountered a wave estimated to be 112 feet high in a typhoon off the Philippines.

Waves in the test tank are beautifully regular. Their dimensions can be controlled, and they can be carefully measured as they proceed in an orderly train down the tank. Such waves can be measured for height (the vertical distance between any trough and the following crest), for period (the time it takes for two successive crests to pass a given point), and for length (the distance between two succeeding crests). It might seem that length and period would be related, and they are; the longer a wave, the faster it will travel. Anybody with a sweep-second hand on his watch can measure the approximate length of a wave—by squaring the period and multiplying by five. Thus a regular wave with a period of 10 seconds is about 500 feet long (10 by 10 by 5).

Complex patterns in the sea

Unfortunately ocean waves are rarely, if ever, simple, single and pure in form. Instead, as a ship meets waves in the open sea, their outstanding, universal characteristic is irregularity. They are an infinitely complex composite of many different wave trains, some large, some small, driven by varying winds from a hundred different points of origin, at different speeds, merging, blending, warring, some dying out, some surviving, overwhelming others and sweeping on before the wind to clash with new waves on the move beyond the horizon.

Indeed, waves at sea seem so chaotic that, until recently, mariners and scientists have despaired of being able to analyze them. Two things have now changed the picture. One is a new mathematical approach to the problem itself. The other is the introduction of computers, which can make innumerable calculations in short time. The new approach was first made by Norbert Wiener, a world-famous mathematician at Massachusetts Institute of Technology. The Institute is near the Charles River, and Wiener was fascinated by the ever-changing patterns of the water. His interest was not purely esthetic, however. "How could one bring to a mathematical regularity the study of the mass of ever shifting ripples and waves . . .?" he wrote. "At one time the waves ran high, flecked with patches of foam, while at another, they were barely noticeable ripples . . . What descriptive language could I use that would portray these clearly visible facts without involving me in the inextricable complexity of a complete description of the water surface. This problem of the waves was clearly one for averaging and statistics . . ." In time Wiener evolved his mathematical tool, spectrum analysis—a means of breaking down complex patterns into a large number of measurable components.

Analyzing the ocean's waves

Wiener was a theorist and never did get around to applying spectrum analysis to the ocean itself, but his ideas were taken up by two oceanographers from New York University, Willard Pierson and Gerhard Neumann, who reasoned that any given irregular area of the sea could be broken down into a number of component parts—into wave trains of different lengths and heights. What they were saying, in effect, was: "Let us forget about trying to measure every wave we see, and its effect on every other wave. We will find out by computer analysis what different kinds of simple waves exist in a certain sea, and assume that the sea consists only of pure waves of those kinds."

In short, spectrum analysis is a kind of simplification. A sample record is taken, and can be made to speak for the whole sea in that area as long as the wind remains steady. Of course, if the sampling is too meager, the resulting spectrum will be crude and inaccurate. Thus, although the end result is to simplify, the technique is complicated. When Pierson and Neumann went out to sea to begin observing waves, they sometimes took as many as 6,000 readings of one small patch of ocean, and these readings were the basis for some 8,000,000 arithmetical calculations by computer. They did this many times and under a variety of conditions of wind and sea, and in time were able to produce a number of different spectra, each describing a different set of conditions, and each represent-

DIRECTION OF WAVE ⟶

AN OCEAN WAVE is formed by the movement of the countless water particles which revolve in circles at and below the surface. This diagram shows the clockwise orbits followed by 13 such particles along the profile of a wave that is moving from left to right. This motion, and the orbital positions the particles occupy at any one time, gives a wave its shape.

ing a key to all the random waves in the area. The exact surface of the sea could never be described by a spectrum, but its general nature could.

This means that a man sitting in an office can, by consulting formulas and tables and making mathematical calculations, tell the condition of the sea—day or night, in any corner of the world—provided he knows what the local wind and weather conditions have been for several hours. More extraordinary still, if he has reliable meteorological forecasts for a couple of days ahead, he can predict with considerable accuracy what the sea *will* be like.

Thrift through mathematics

The practical results from the use of these new mathematical tools have been impressive. Merchant ships, traveling back and forth between England and the East Coast of the United States have been able to shorten their average passage time by a day by following the "least-time track"—that is, choosing the best compromise between delays from heavy seas and delays from increasing the distance traveled. The U.S. Military Sea Transport Service estimates that plotting courses with the aid of spectra has meant savings of one million dollars per year.

But is mere avoidance of rough seas the best way to exploit this marvelous technique of wave analysis? Why can it not be applied directly to hull design so that ships can deal with bad weather instead of having to go around it? Theoretically it can, and theory is already beginning to be put into practice. But the problem is not as simple as it appears. For one thing, a ship has six different motions that must be dealt with. These are: *roll* (tipping from side to side); *pitch* (seesawing up and down); *yaw* (fishtailing to produce a zigzag course); *heave* (lifting up and down of the hull); *surge* (speeding up and slowing down as the ship rides a wave); and *sway* (moving of the whole ship to one side or the other). Of these, rolling and pitching present the greatest problems.

Every ship has its own rolling period—the time it takes to roll freely from starboard to port and back again, a measure of its own internal rhythm. It can roll just a little, or it can roll wildly, until its rail goes under; but the time the roll takes will be the same. In this respect it is like a pendulum; the farther the pendulum swings, the faster it goes.

A ship's rolling period is determined by the shape of its hull, its beam, and the distribution of weight. Rolling becomes a matter of concern when wave periods coincide with a ship's natural rolling period. When the waves are fairly regular, a minor change of course or speed usually ends synchronous rolling. However, as the sea grows rougher and more irregular an interesting phenomenon frequently takes place: the ship begins to respond to component waves with frequencies that match its own internal rhythm. In such circumstances these particular wave trains

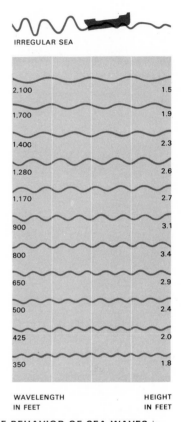

IRREGULAR SEA

WAVELENGTH IN FEET	HEIGHT IN FEET
2,100	1.5
1,700	1.9
1,400	2.3
1,280	2.6
1,170	2.7
900	3.1
800	3.4
650	2.9
500	2.4
425	2.0
350	1.8

THE BEHAVIOR OF SEA WAVES is irregular *(top)*, but when they are analyzed by a computer they can be separated into many individual and orderly component waves, as shown. Since each of these waves can be measured, a mathematical picture, or "spectrum," can be plotted from them that accurately describes the sea's actual behavior.

A ROLLING MOTION, one of six motions caused by waves, is shown in the diagram above. Roll occurs when waves approach a vessel from the side, causing it to rock back and forth. Stabilizing devices, such as fixed bilge keels, antirolling tanks or hull fins, are now used on most modern ships to reduce this motion.

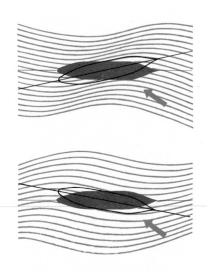

A YAWING MOTION takes place if waves approach a ship at an angle from either bow or stern, causing it to change heading. These two drawings show a hull from directly above, swung first to the left *(outline)* by the crest of a wave and then to the right by the trough. The wave is moving in the direction shown by the arrows.

keep hitting the side of the ship just as it is starting its roll, and under this constant nudging the motion of the ship soon builds up to a dangerous degree. The principle is the same as that used by a man giving his child a ride in a swing, when he builds up the arc of the swing by giving it a small push each time that its downward motion starts. When the sea does this to a ship a much more drastic change of course or rate of speed must be made to break the motion.

Ailerons for a ship

Today most modern vessels are equipped with antirolling devices of one kind or another. The most effective of those now in use are gyro-controlled stabilizing fins, standard equipment on all but a few of the large liners now in service. The mechanism functions on the same principle as the ailerons of an airplane.

About midships on each side of the vessel, a fin projects from the hull well below the waterline. The fins are hinged, and operate in opposite directions. When the ship starts to roll, sensitive electrically driven gyroscopes inside the vessel respond to both the degree and velocity of the movement, and apply corrective tilts to the fins. If the roll is to starboard, the forward edge of the fin on that side turns upward. The pressure of the water running past pushes upward against the fin, and the tendency of the vessel to roll further in that direction is checked. Simultaneously, the fin on the port side turns downward, and the oncoming water exerts downward pressure. The coupled action of the two forces creates a powerful righting effect. When the roll is to port, the tilt of the fins is reversed. The gyroscopes work with such speed and accuracy that the roll is usually quenched before it can develop. Hydraulic machinery, similar to that which operates the landing gear on an airplane, retracts the fins inside the hull when they are not needed.

Unfortunately, stabilizing fins take up too much space to be practical for cargo vessels, and most of them have nonmovable fins called bilge keels fastened to their hulls. These perform much the same function as stabilizing fins but are not as efficient. Also used are antirolling tanks—a pair of tanks, one on each side of the ship, each half filled with water and connected together by a narrow conduit. As the vessel starts to roll to port, the water in the starboard tank begins to flow in the same direction, but this movement is slowed by the narrowness of the pipe. By the time most of the water from the starboard tank is on the other side, the ship has started to roll the other way, but the weight of the water, now in the port tank, slows the motion. This constant time lag in movement of the water from tank to tank markedly reduces the rolling of the ship.

Pitching, an uphill-downhill movement when a ship is riding the

A PITCHING MOTION is the result of wave action that sends a vessel's bow and stern seesawing up and down. It is worst when the ship is driving into a rough head sea—climbing up one steep wave and slamming down into the trough of the next. In extremely heavy seas, a ship may totally submerge its bow in a wave, as in the diagram at right.

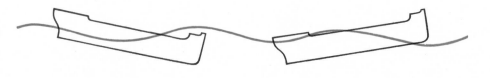

waves, is a far more serious problem than rolling and is the crux of the problem of achieving completely reliable, all-weather scheduling today. The question is not one of increased power, of driving the ship forward harder and harder as the waves try to beat it back, but of designing hull forms that will pitch less when speeding into a rough head sea. Interestingly, the same techniques of spectrum analysis that have revealed so much about waves can also be applied to the ships themselves. Pierson and Manley St. Denis have shown that, just as in the case of rolling, a ship in an irregular sea pitches mainly to the component waves that are tuned to its internal pitching rhythm. But there is an important difference: waves shorter than the ship will not make it pitch, even though they are in synchronism with its natural pitching period.

Therefore, a designer can forget about all waves in the spectrum that are shorter than the hull he is designing, and worry only about ones that are as long or longer. If he can design a hull that will behave well in those waves, then he can be sure that it will behave satisfactorily in the confused heaving sea that is the result of all those waves put together. Furthermore, he knows that the longer he can make his ship, the longer will be the critical wave and the faster she can go before pitching becomes violent. This basic rule has been proved many times by actually lengthening the hulls of ships and observing that they can maintain much higher speeds in head seas than they could before.

Theoretically, then, all ships should be very long. However, length is expensive, and there is a practical limit to the size of most vessels. Other approaches to the problem of pitching are needed, and, once again, these are supplied in the test tank.

Testing with man-made storms

In such research centers as the U.S. Navy's Taylor Model Basin, and in the Davidson Laboratory at Stevens Institute of Technology, pneumatic computer-controlled wave-makers can now simulate sea states ranging from a light squall to a tempest. Batteries of sensitive electronic gauges and recorders follow every response of the miniature hulls as they pitch, heave and roll in the turbulent water. By comparing various hull designs at different speeds and headings in regular waves of various lengths, engineers can predict the probability of slamming or wet decks for each ship in a wide variety of sea conditions. Furthermore, they provide a means of checking theories that ultimately may permit the answers to be obtained by electronic computers—without the building of models at all. In short, the model centers are becoming so sophisticated that they are threatening to put themselves out of business.

But that is a matter for the future. There are still many areas of investigation that are suited to the discipline of the test tank. One such

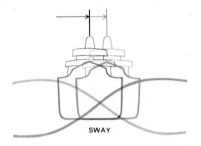

SWAY

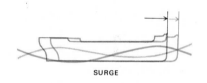

SURGE

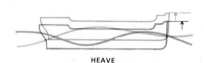

HEAVE

SWAY, SURGE AND HEAVE, depicted above, are three of the six motions caused by waves. The illustrations in green indicate changes in a ship's position that take place during these movements. Sway is a lateral motion that occurs when a ship shifts from side to side on successive waves *(top)*. Surge is longitudinal motion of a vessel as it speeds up and slows down when waves travel the length of its hull *(middle)*. Heave is a ship's vertical movement in response to the rise and fall of waves *(bottom)*. These movements, along with roll, yaw and pitch, always occur in various combinations.

is the testing of antipitching devices, and the Taylor Basin has done considerable work with another kind of fin. This is a projection like a small airplane wing sticking out from each side of the bow, and located well below the surface of the water. Model tests with bow fins promised such a dramatic reduction of pitching at speeds of over 15 knots, that it was decided to try full-size experiments with a Mariner-type cargo vessel. Sea tests so far have revealed that pitching is reduced by about 20 per cent in irregular seas kicked up by 24-knot winds. In rougher seas created by 40-knot winds the reduction in pitching is still a respectable 13 per cent.

One major problem remains to be solved, however. As the fin approaches the surface of the water, a large "ventilated bubble" filled with air forms beneath the fin. The subsequent collapse of the bubble causes the ship to vibrate. Tests with various modifications of the fin are now going on.

Seeking solutions to new problems and better ways of dealing with old ones will always be the goals of the men who build ships. But thanks to advances in naval architecture pioneered by William Froude's brilliant concept of model-testing, and the application of theoretical mathematics, the work will proceed more quickly and with greater assurance of success than ever before in history.

Tiny Ships
on
Indoor Oceans

For thousands of years the only way to test a new ship design was to try it out at sea. Since ships sometimes sank in the process, men thought twice before experimenting. Then, in the 1870s, a new method was introduced: testing scale models in small indoor basins. Today these laboratories check out everything from warships to seaplanes. In its basins, the Davidson Laboratory of the Stevens Institute of Technology has improved hull performance in heavy seas, determined the most efficient hull design for a given speed, and helped bring the U.S. an America's Cup victory. Test basins have had to reckon with many details. Because the fresh water they use is less buoyant than salt water, they have to make up the difference mathematically. Their computations must even account for the fact that the viscosity of water cannot be reduced to conform to the size of the models. But the test basins have paid off with near-revolutionary advances in design.

TEMPEST IN A TEST TANK
Tossed on "mountainous" seas, a laminated-pine model of a 400-foot cargo ship attempts to turn in a test tank at Davidson Laboratory. Such realistically irregular, wind-whipped waves—called Sea State Six by seamen—are rarely produced in the tanks. Usually experimenters try to isolate all the component waves of a sea condition and expose a model to different waves one at a time.

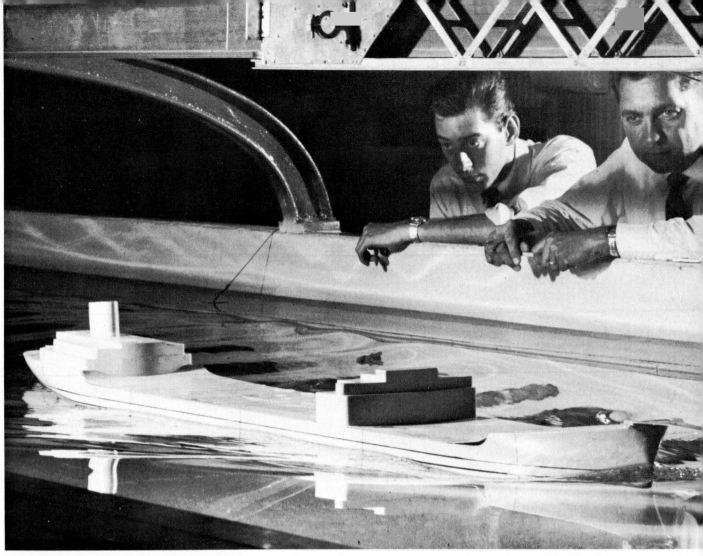

WATCHING A SMOOTH CROSSING

Two engineers study the waves created by a model of a 550-foot tanker as it is towed past. The vertical rod pulling the model is attached to an overhead carriage riding in steel tracks. The test tank is protected from sunlight to prevent the growth of algae. Experts discovered to their surprise that for some reason algae may reduce water resistance by as much as 20 per cent. It was found that adding certain

A model oil tanker proceeds down the 141-foot-long resistance-testing tank, creating waves as it goes. Its speeds in the sequence of pictures

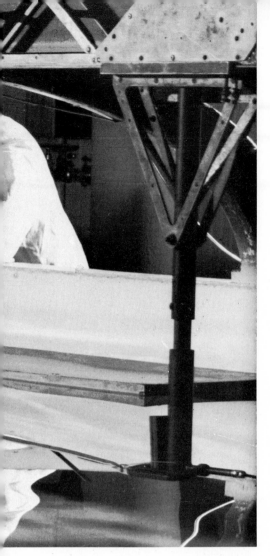

chemicals to the water will produce the same effect. Test-tank engineers are studying the phenomenon, but so far it remains unexplained.

The High Cost of Making Waves

From barge to racing shell, every vessel creates waves. Experts can judge roughly, from the size of the waves angling away from a model, how much of the engine's power is being wasted in generating them. (Another major power drain is the resistance of hull friction.)

Wave-making resistance does not increase uniformly with the speed of a ship. Instead, it takes a sudden upward leap after a certain speed has been reached. Beyond this maximum efficient speed—represented by the fourth point on the graph at right and in the fourth picture below—exorbitant amounts of fuel or engine power are required to offset wave resistance. The critical speed naturally varies according to hull length and shape. A ship with a long and narrow hull will have low wave-making resistance but will be expensive to build. Today no designer would think of building a hull or ordering an engine before verifying his calculations of wave-making resistance by model test. Often several different models of his ship are tested and compared before the best design is picked out.

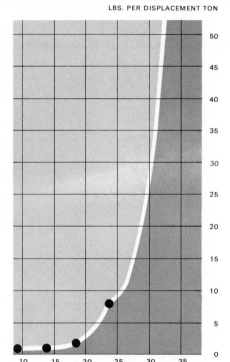

LBS. PER DISPLACEMENT TON

A CHART OF RISING RESISTANCE

A graph of the wave-making resistance of the tanker below indicates that it can cruise economically up to a speed of 23.6 knots—after which the price of making waves soars. The four speeds shown in the picture sequence below are represented by dots on the graph curve.

are exactly equivalent to 9.5, 14.2, 19 and 23.6 knots. The waves made by the model become steadily larger but fewer as its speed rises.

A POWER-PACKED LOAD
Carefully simulating proper cargo-loading, a technician arranges the batteries that will drive a model's electric motor. A hull which has no superstructure is adequate for a turning test.

A Design for Turning

When a captain orders, "Right full rudder," how fast does his ship turn? The answer depends on a number of design factors. Tank tests have shown that a ship's maneuverability is affected by hull shape, propeller power, rudder silhouette, heel angle at turns, and even cargo-loading. A ship that presents a smaller broadside area at the stern is easier to turn. A larger rudder will turn a ship faster, and its shape may control heeling. Testing of models can accurately determine the diameter of the turning circle of a ship, and help a designer adjust factors to meet the needs of his vessel—whether it be a sluggish tanker or a swift-turning PT boat.

A MECHANICAL CAPTAIN
The guidance mechanism is programmed for whatever rudder movements may be desired during the test. The propeller of this model is scaled down dimensionally, like the hull. But it must run at higher rpm's than the propeller of the full-sized ship for equivalent power output.

EXAMINING A MODEL WAKE
Engineers study the path of a model as it turns at high speed. The white barrier at the upper right is a mechanical wave maker, made of plastic foam coated with fiber glass. Driven by an electric motor, it can create any wave pattern by thrusting up and down in the water.

A Hidden Peril in Stormy Seas

On December 18, 1944, three U.S. destroyers steaming along near the Philippines were caught in a typhoon. As the vessels were assaulted by increasingly huge waves and fierce winds, their rolling grew more and more exaggerated—until the leaning reached 70°, water poured down the stacks and all three ships vanished.

The fatal rolling of these destroyers was a nightmarish example of the phenomenon known as synchronism. The problems of synchronism have not yet been fully solved. Tests of models have shown that even a large ship is like a pendulum: if set in rocking motion—side to side, or bow to stern—it will continue to oscillate at a natural frequency of roll or pitch that depends on hull shape and loading. When waves strike the ship at the same frequency—in synchronism —the rocking will be amplified, perhaps to dangerous levels.

In the open ocean, the synchronous swells are usually indistinguishable amid irregular, wind-tossed seas. But with test tanks and wave makers, experimenters can choose any wave frequency and size their studies require. They have found that waves less than three quarters as long as a ship will not produce extreme pitching, even when they synchronize with the ship's own motion. Hence, designing ships with greater length helps diminish the problem of pitching. Other anti-synchronism designs include spinning gyro-stabilizers, fixed fins near the bow to "dampen" pitching, and movable fins amidships to offset rolling. These innovations, perfected in the tanks, made possible higher speeds and greater comfort in rough seas.

LABORING IN THE OPEN SEA
Stern buried, bow uplifted, a U.S. destroyer on Atlantic duty slams into a wave as its pitching motion reaches a high point. At Davidson Laboratory, parabolic, or sloping, beaches are installed at one end of the tanks to absorb their artificially made waves. Without them, the waves might reflect back into the test tanks and produce a hopelessly confused sea.

MEASURING WAVE DAMAGE
A technician watches intently as a model destroyer pitches on long waves—the sort that may damage the hull structure. The model has been cut into sections at the white lines and reconnected with calibrated metal bars which permit hull stresses to be measured electronically.

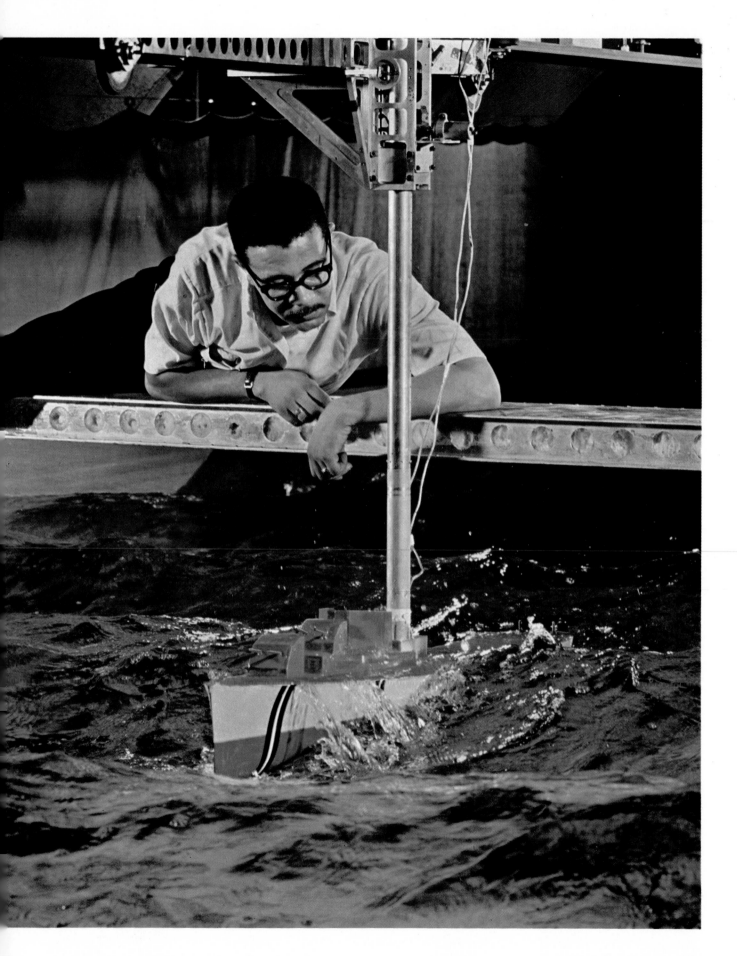

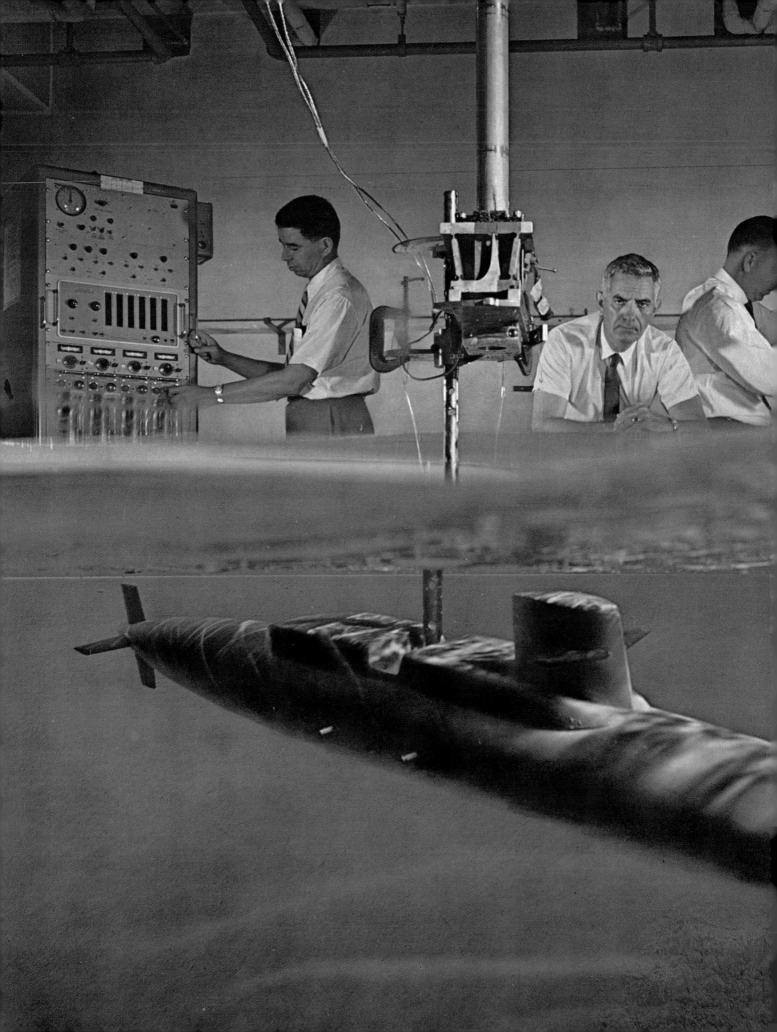

Keeping Balance under the Sea

A submarine underwater has many of the same balancing problems as an airplane in flight. It must be able to dive, climb and turn within a fluid medium. During maneuvers its stability may be adversely affected by currents and by ballast changes made to control depth—and by the subsurface surges of waves.

Stability is an especially urgent matter for a nuclear Polaris sub such as the 380-foot *George Washington*, shown on these pages being tested in model form. The *George Washington* is, in effect, built around a 128-foot-long undersea launching pad that is designed to shoot 16 missiles surface-ward in the space of a few minutes. The sub has a computer system to synchronize its missile-firing with its rolling beneath the waves.

Davidson Laboratory was assigned the task of testing the submarine to find its extremes of motion, and thus establish the demands to be faced by the computer. In the 1/80 scale model, specific weights—representing 105,000 feet of pipes, 70 miles of cable, and so on—had to be precisely located to simulate the real submarine's center of gravity. The job of load-adjustment took more than a month and pushed the cost of the model beyond $5,000. But that sum assured the missile-launching reliability of a $100 million submarine.

A SUB TETHERED FOR TESTING
Engineers adjust the electronic apparatus used to record wave pressure on a model of the submarine *George Washington*, held in fixed position beneath the surface. Precision weights embedded in a plastic-foam filling balance the model when it is being put through motion tests.

THE CHURNING UNDERSEA
As a wave passes from left to right across its beam, the model of the *George Washington* rolls in both directions *(top to bottom)*. One of the principal stability problems of a submarine is created by the diminished but disruptive effect of waves below the surface. At a depth equal to half its length, a wave still has approximately 4 per cent of its surface movement.

49

Shaping a Racing Champion

In the 1964 America's Cup race, the U.S. 12-meter yacht *Constellation* outsailed Britain's *Sovereign* four times in a row. While *Constellation* sliced cleanly through the choppy seas off Newport, *Sovereign* was left far behind. At least part of the credit for *Constellation*'s prowess goes to the Davidson Laboratory, where the yacht's designer, Olin Stephens, had been perfecting racing yachts since the 1930s.

Like much of the military research done at Davidson, experiments with competitive yachts are conducted under strict security conditions. No information was divulged about actual details of the *Constellation*'s design. However, the methods used to test the development model *(below)* were

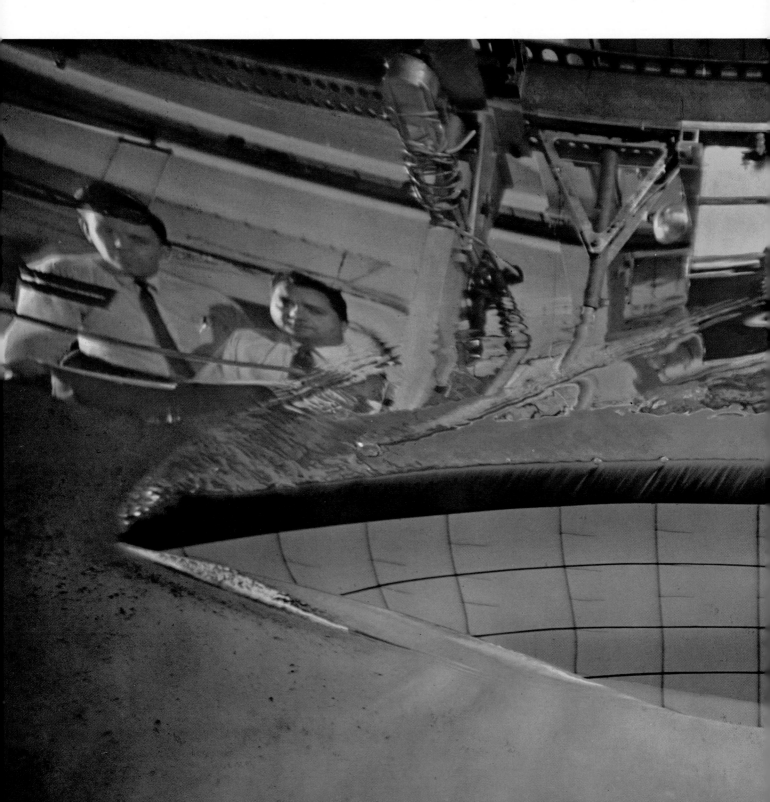

not kept secret. To observe the flow pattern of water past the model, technicians painted a grid on the hull, embedded tufts of string in the wood and took extensive films. So that resistance could be simulated, a strip of sand was glued near the bow to create water turbulence. In such precision tests, the yacht was proved efficient before it ever touched water.

VICTORY'S SLEEK SILHOUETTE
Photographed through a porthole at the bottom of the test tank, the development model of the *Constellation* glides across the surface at a 20° heel. Because of new racing regulations, foreign countries are not permitted to test their competitive yachts at Davidson Laboratory.

3

Days
of
Sail

CADETS CLIMB THE RIGGING OF THE WEST GERMAN BARK *GORCH FOCK*, ONE OF THE FEW REMAINING SQUARE-RIGGERS.

ON A JULY MORNING IN 1964, twenty-three sailing ships flying the flags of 13 nations sailed up New York Harbor, past the soaring towers of Manhattan, to an anchorage near the George Washington Bridge. Twelve of the vessels were fore-and-aft rigged schooners, but 11 were what the newspapers described as "tall ships"—square-rigged craft, barks and barkentines, white-hulled, stately, seemingly from another age.

These 11 square-rigged vessels were naval and merchant-marine training ships, most of them steel-hulled and built since World War II. Their dramatic rendezvous, called "Operation Sail," had taken four years of planning. Oldtimers along the New York waterfront vowed that its like would never be seen again. It was the last time, and the last place, for a gathering of the world's vanishing windjammers, numbering probably fewer than 20.

Perhaps the observers are right, but the windship and the windboat certainly live on in other forms. On any summer weekend, Long Island Sound from City Island to New London, San Francisco Bay from Redwood City to the Golden Gate, and a hundred other harbors, coves, rivers, lakes and estuaries are white with leaning sails. Sails still move Arab dhows along the shores of the Persian Gulf; they propel Chinese junks and Ceylonese outriggers, Egyptian *gyassas* and the *lakatois* of southern New Guinea. "The sail," wrote Claude Farrère, "will not die as long as men demand their bread and their pleasure from the sea. . . . There will always be sailors, because there will always be fishermen, yachtsmen and men who love the waves, the wind and the sound and swell of the sea."

No one knows to this day how, where or when man first invented or stumbled upon the remarkable concept of the sail. Technically it is an airfoil, a kind of wing, for gathering and applying the wind's power to the lever of the mast—man's first means of harnessing a natural force to do his work. Perhaps, weary from stroking his dugout across a Central American lake, an Indian, simply by chance, rested his paddle on the floor of his craft, blade in the air, felt the pull of the breeze, and let it carry him and the boat before it. A thousand years earlier (or later, who knows?) on the Nile or on the Malabar Coast, a man may have seen a vagrant breeze blow a curled leaf across a pool; perhaps this phenomenon inspired him to fashion a crude square sail of matting, bark or linen for his boat.

Wherever or whenever it happened, the sail was a prodigious step forward. With the sail to help him, man could make his craft bigger, heavier than before. He could transport more people and goods, embark on longer journeys. The waters along his coasts became highways. Horizons beckoned. The seas were suddenly pathways to islands and hitherto unattainable shores.

As man's use of the sea developed down through the ages, he learned more about ships. The long, enthralling story of these windships falls into three distinct phases, defined by man's successive demands for (1) transport for inland seas and coastal waters; (2) transport plus distance-capability; and then (3) transport plus distance-capability plus speed.

The first phase ranged from about 4000 B.C. to 1440 A.D. It was represented by several evolutionary series of ships culminating in the "southern" merchant sailer of the Mediterranean and the "northern" single-masted cog of the North and Baltic Seas. The second phase extended from 1440 to 1840 and was represented by the full-rigged ship in its many forms. The final phase ranged from 1840 to the twilight of tall ships in the 1890s. It was represented by sailing's crowning triumph, the clipper ship.

The wide-ranging Carthaginians

Slender, oared, sailing ships of the Egyptians fared 300 miles northwest to Crete as early as 3000 B.C. By 500 B.C. ships of Hanno the Carthaginian had returned from Africa's west coast with gorilla-head trophies on their stems, and other Carthaginian ships were sailing to far-off Britain for tin. However, it was not until about 200 A.D.—and the development of the stout Roman merchantman—that the southern, or Mediterranean, ship attained a relatively stable level of design.

Roman biremes—long, ram-beaked fighting ships with two tiers of oars on each side—had cleared the Mediterranean of pirates. Now Rome herself demanded vast supplies of imports—ivory, wine, oil, metals, textiles, precious stones and, above all, grain. Most of the goods came by merchantmen from every corner of the known world, from Tunisia and Spain, from Britain and northern Gaul, the Black Sea, Egypt and Asia Minor. Two carvings, one on a Pompeian tomb circa 50 B.C. and another at Ostia, the Roman port at the Tiber's mouth, circa 200 A.D., agree in all but minor detail on the features of the typical merchantman of the era.

She was about 100 feet long and 30 feet wide, apparently already adhering to the conventional 3-to-1 ratio of length to breadth which would still be used a thousand years later. Her hull was solidly built and, when viewed in cross section, was rounded rather than square or flat-bottomed. Her construction also followed a tradition that is still in vogue for wooden ships. First, a strong keel was laid down, ribs were then attached at regular intervals from bow to stern. To the ribs was fastened her outer planking, held in place with bronze nails and laid edge to edge, "carvel" fashion, rather than overlapping like shingles, as in the "clinker-built" style of the northern ship. Along her side were three or more wales, extra-heavy planks to strengthen the hull and protect it from chafing when lying at a dock. She had a high stern for lifting to a following sea, and an ornamental sternpost, usually carved to represent a swan's throat and head, facing aft. Near the stern was a deckhouse whose roof served as a bridge for the steersman. Her bow was relatively low. She probably measured some 120 tons and had her bottom sheathed in lead to protect her from teredos, destructive wood-boring marine mollusks. The Roman merchantman had one mast placed amidships and a square mainsail hanging from a straight yard. Mast and

NATIVE SAILBOATS still cleave the coastal waters of the East in spite of today's predominance of the powered ship. One example is a swift Ceylonese dugout *(top)* which has an outrigger for stability and two masts that support a square sail. Another is the bizarre *lakatoi* of New Guinea *(bottom),* which for its annual tribal trading voyages is ceremonially rigged with two tasseled sails shaped like crab claws.

sail were both traditional and harked back as far as the seagoing Egyptian craft of 3000 B.C. Like many ancient ships, she was steered by a pair of rudders, one on each side of the stern and each controlled by a tiller, angling inboard from the top of the rudder post.

One innovation lacking in older Greek and Egyptian ships was a new system of "brails," vertical ropes passing through rings sewn to the sail which made it possible to furl, or shorten, the sail from the bottom, much as a venetian blind is raised. Also new was a pair of triangular topsails that could be raised above the main yard to help out in light winds. A final noteworthy innovation, and also a direct hint of the two-master to come, was a long spar raking sharply forward over the bow —something between a mast and a bowsprit. On this was set a small sail called an artemon. Because of its forward placement, it helped keep the ship before the wind and thus was more of a steering aid than a pulling sail.

Of course, she had to deal with a built-in problem common to square-sailed vessels: she could not go upwind effectively. A square sail has limited maneuverability. Set at right angles to the ship, it is most efficient when the wind is blowing directly from astern. It is true that the yard (or pole) from which the sail hangs can be slightly angled to one side or the other, permitting the vessel to change course accordingly. But if this change is too great, forward motion will stop and the ship will merely be blown sideways. The closest that an ancient square-rigged vessel could sail to the wind was slightly better than a right angle. Even as late as the 17th Century, during some of the greatest days of square sail, ocean voyaging was largely a "downhill" affair: the wind had to be blowing in the general direction the captain wanted to go if he were to make significant progress.

The zigzagging "Latin"

What freed the windship from the crippling limitation of the square rig was the introduction of a new kind of sail, the lateen. It gets its name from the French word *latine*, or Latin, because vessels with that rig were first seen by Western Europeans in the Mediterranean. Shaped like a triangle, it is rigged to a long yard which hangs at a slant from a short mast. What makes this sail different from a square one is that it can be swung much farther from the athwart-ship position of its predecessor, until its yard is almost in a line with the long axis of the ship itself. This gives it the name of a "fore-and-aft" sail and makes it the forerunner of virtually every sail in use in the world today. Nothing essentially new in sails has been invented since. What made it so revolutionary was its greater freedom in being trimmed fore-and-aft, for this enabled a ship so rigged to sail closer to the wind—at considerably better than a right angle to it. With this capability, a vessel could "tack" into the wind, angling first on one course, then on another, climbing upwind as a highway zigzags up the side of a mountain.

The beginnings of the lateen rig are lost in the dimness of the early

A SAILING BARGE, the Egyptian *gyassa*, still shuttles goods up and down the Nile River. Unlike the square-sailed boats of ancient Egypt, the *gyassa* has two triangular lateen sails hoisted on two short masts. Its customary procedure is to sail up the Nile with the prevailing north wind and then drift downstream with the current.

Middle Ages. Some marine historians believe that it was invented in the East Indies, or that it may represent a modification of the lugsail of the Chinese junk. Others think that the rig first appeared in the Arabian Sea —where it is still in use today on the Arab dhow—or on the Nile, and that it spread with Mohammedanism across the Mediterranean to Spain and Portugal in the Seventh and Eighth Centuries. The first record of the sail appears in Greek manuscripts dated about 886 A.D. The drawings show single-masted lateeners in striking detail. Their impact upon southern ship design was enormous. By the late Crusades in the 13th Century, almost every ship out of a home port on the Mediterranean was a one-, two- or three-masted lateener.

A longship for Vikings

Meanwhile, from the primitive coracles and dugouts of Britain and Scandinavia, different kinds of ships had been evolving along the North and Baltic Seas and the English Channel. The most important was the Viking longship, and thanks to the Norse custom of interring the ships in burial mounds along with their chiefs, we have a good idea of what she was like. One of the best preserved, excavated near Gokstad in 1880 and now on view at Oslo, was a long, light, slender, double-ended ship, clinker-built, i.e., with a hull made of overlapping planks. Her keel was over 60 feet, and she was nearly 80 feet long overall. Her beam was about 17 feet, her depth not quite seven feet. She had 16 openings, or ports, along each side for oars; round wooden discs covered them and kept out water when she was under sail and heeling. Since remnants of shields covering the oar ports were found on the Gokstad ship, nearly every representation of a Viking ship under sail has shown them, though it is almost certain that they hung there only for display in calm weather. Oarsmen would have to remove them before they could row; under sail, any sea at all would have carried them away.

The single mast of a Viking ship was stepped about three feet forward of amidships. She raised a square sail, often brightly painted and made, most likely, of homespun reinforced with diagonal strips of linen or leather. Like all northern double-enders, she was fitted with one rudder —a long, straight blade, controlled by a tiller slotted at right angles into the rudderhead. The tiller was located on the right side of the stern, a placement which explains how the term "starboard," a corruption of "steer board," or steering side, came to mean the right side of a ship. The term "port" was applied to the left side because the crew always tied up the ship in port with this rudderless side against the quay. Larboard, another term for the left side, came from the word "ladeborde," the loading board, where cargo was received.

There are indications that the Vikings learned to adapt the square sail to sailing in a beam wind. In a representation of one of William the Conqueror's Norman ships in the Bayeux tapestry, the mast is fitted with shrouds, ropes to give it lateral support. Historians infer that these made it possible for the sail to be shifted to a position lengthwise with the vessel—almost to the position of a fore-and-aft sail—thus exerting a side-ward pressure against the mast.

Such ships were fast, beautifully modeled for moving through the water with a minimum of resistance. In 1893, a full-scale replica of the Gokstad ship crossed the Atlantic in about 28 days, logging as high as 10 knots during the passage.

But as the influence of the Vikings declined, and seaborne trade increased in the north, commerce demanded a sturdier, less capricious, more workaday vessel than the graceful longship. Hulls, while remaining clinker-built, became deeper, with more cargo capacity. Ultimately two other improvements were added: a true stern rudder, which replaced the steering blade and improved handling; and a bowsprit.

By the start of the 14th Century, these developments had generalized into a relatively standard, eminently workable northern ship called a cog. This craft was destined to exert profound influence on the next 400 years of waterborne transport and on the history of civilization itself.

The cog sailed into the Mediterranean to stay in the early 1300s. A pirate ship of her type from Bayonne in southwestern France is believed to have invaded southern waters. Her capacity and rugged sturdiness appealed at once to the merchants of Genoa, Venice and Barcelona. Soon she began to replace the two-masted and three-masted lateeners called caravels. It was inevitable that the best features of both types would be combined. The stage was now set for the full-rigged ship—the far-sailing vessels of Columbus and da Gama, Magellan and Drake.

Closed land, open sea

It was not the confluence of northern and southern technology alone that inspired the *Santa Maria* and raised the curtain on the second phase of the windship's history. Discovery was in the air. Portuguese mariners had pushed down the west coast of Africa to the Cape of Good Hope. The Atlantic islands—the Canaries and Azores—were settled. Men of learning knew that the world was round. They had crude but serviceable instruments of navigation: the magnetic compass, the cross-staff for determining latitude, primitive logs and sounding leads. But one force more than all of these speeded the advent of a ship with distance capability—and that was the need to explore to the west, across the open ocean. For the old land route to the fabulous riches and spices of the Indies had been closed by the rise of Islam.

Constantinople had fallen to the Turks in 1453. It was but a matter of time before they would conquer Egypt. The traditional routes to the Levant, to India, the Indies and Cathay were no longer available to the modern Westernized world just emerging from the Middle Ages—to the bold, assertive, self-conscious and life-conscious men of the Renaissance. They needed a ship to sail in—to sail out of sight of land in—one that would get them across a sea and back again. And, ultimately, the shipwrights of Spain and Portugal gave it to them.

Spanish and Portuguese shipbuilders had, for some time, been disenchanted with the all-lateen-rigged caravels because shifting to another tack required raising the long, cumbersome yard to the vertical and throwing it behind and to the other side of the mast so that the sail could fill out on the opposite side. Moreover, the lateen sail was not nearly so efficient in following winds as the square sail. In a burst of inventiveness and creativity, the shipwrights combined the caravel with the cog and produced the first, classic full-rigged ship: three masts, with large square sails on foremast and mainmast; a lateen sail set on the mizzen; and, frequently, a rather large spritsail set forward of the stem, below the bowsprit.

A mixture of elements

This ship had an interesting combination of features, some anticipating the future, others reflecting antiquity. Her spritsail, for instance, probably was the modified artemon of a Roman merchantman. Her hull had the carvel build of the southern ship, and the roundness, the stern rudder and the great mainmast of the northern craft. For ease of handling, her sails began to be broken down into smaller, more manageable units. Instead of there being one sail on a mast, there were two: a large mainsail with a smaller topsail above it.

The topsail was to catch light air; the main courses were the driving sails. With this rig the new vessel of the 15th and 16th Centuries could sail to within 65 degrees of the wind.

She was a ship of history. Victor Hugo called her "one of the great masterpieces of man." She could carry a large supply of stores and thus was capable of remaining at sea continuously for months on end. She could circle the globe, as indeed she did in the 16th Century—and she was so true and sound a ship that mariners and shipwrights together found no significant way to improve her for the next 400 years.

Though no drawings or specifications survive, we know that Columbus' flagship, the *Santa Maria*, was such a ship. So was the *Pinta*, and so, after her rerigging from a three-masted lateener, was the Admiral's favorite, the *Niña*, except that she carried no topsail or spritsail.

According to the classic rule of thumb, a ship's beam, length of keel and overall length should be in the proportions 1:2:3. Going only on the hint that the *Santa Maria* was perhaps 80 tons—in the literal sense of having a capacity of about 80 barrels, or "tuns," of wine—historians see her as possessing about the following dimensions: overall length, 78.5 feet; length of keel, 55.5 feet; beam, 26 feet. They guess that she may have drawn 6.5 feet.

Other contemporary features must have been present: wooden pegs, or treenails, for holding planking to frames; the bottom covered with a tallow-pitch mixture to protect it from teredos; ballast of stone or sand for stability; a wooden hand pump for clearing leakage water from the bilges; hempen rope rigging; an arched deck to clear away shipped water; a long wooden tiller projecting forward into the ship through a hole high in the stern to an area beneath the poop deck. The helmsman

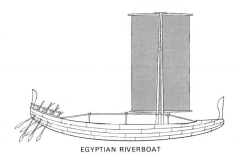

EGYPTIAN RIVERBOAT

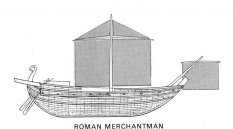

ROMAN MERCHANTMAN

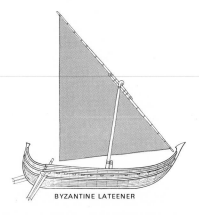

BYZANTINE LATEENER

SOUTHERN SHIP DEVELOPMENT, shown by these drawings, began about 2500 B.C. with the square-sailed Egyptian riverboat, steered by several pairs of oars. In the Roman ship of about 200 A.D., these oars were reduced to a single pair; the ship carried small topsails above its mainsail and a steering sail that hung from a bowsprit. Like its forerunners, the Byzantine vessel of the Ninth Century was "carvel-built"—i.e., its hull was fashioned from planks joined smoothly top to bottom. But it bore a notable innovation —a triangular lateen sail that allowed the vessel to sail close to the wind.

stood in there, between decks. He could see nothing of sea or sails and steered only by compass and by the feel of the ship beneath his feet, or on orders from the officer of the watch on the deck above.

Columbus' trio of small ships of this type made the Atlantic crossing in 69 days, averaging four knots. His biographer, Samuel Eliot Morison, who retraced the Admiral's route four and a half centuries later, wrote in his *Admiral of the Ocean Sea:* "Anyone could design better seagoing vessels and rig them better today, but the gain would be largely in comfort, labor-saving and safety, not in speed. The *Niña, Pinta* and *Santa Maria* were well built, well rigged and well manned. . . . They were fine ships, competent for their allotted tasks."

The introduction of heavy guns aboard ship (a ship was first sunk by gunfire in 1513) led to interesting changes. Heretofore, a warship wishing to engage another in battle had to sail close alongside so that her soldiers could attack the enemy directly with boarding parties. Centuries of this kind of naval warfare led to the gradual development of higher and higher ends to warships, as commanders tried to gain height over their adversaries and also to have places to retreat to in case their own ship was successfully boarded. Cannon rendered these built-up ends meaningless; today only the names remain—forecastle and aftercastle.

Through the 17th and 18th Centuries, ships grew larger, and rigging masters were busy flinging up tiers of three, four and sometimes five sails on masts that grew ever higher and were now constructed in three sections. To counterbalance the great increase of square-sail surface, some additional fore-and-aft sail area was necessary, and this was provided by staysails—small triangular sails like sparless lateens set on stays between the masts. Eventually these small triangular sails began appearing on stays that ran down from the foremast to the bow of the ship, or to an extension of the bowsprit known as the jibboom, in which case they were called jibs. Jibs were much more efficient and easier to handle than the cumbersome spritsail hanging down below the bowsprit and soon replaced it. Still another device for drawing on canvas, particularly in light wind, was commonplace by this time: the studding sail, or "stuns'l," a winglike extension on each side of the square sail.

Thus, at the opening of the 19th Century, almost 400 years after the emergence of the full-rigged ship, we find a standard windship that—although marvelously refined—is still basically the same as her revolutionary predecessor of the Renaissance.

A ship for a new age

But the situation could not remain static for long. The Industrial Revolution was under way. One by one, barriers to free trade between West and East fell away. There were other stirring events that also affected shipping—the discovery of California gold in 1848, of Australian gold in 1851. The world—at least the emergent Machine Age world of the West—needed new ships. Speed was now an important factor. Tea spoiled in the hold if the passage from China took too long. To the

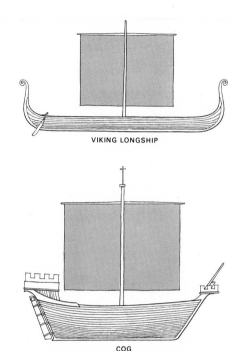

VIKING LONGSHIP

COG

NORTHERN SHIP DEVELOPMENT begins with the Ninth Century Viking ship. Unlike southern vessels, it had a single starboard rudder and a nearly symmetrical "clinker-built" hull—i.e., one made of planks that overlapped instead of joining top to bottom. The 13th Century cog had castles fore and aft, and a rudder in the stern. When it sailed into the Mediterranean two centuries later, its features merged with the lateen rig and carvel hull of the southern tradition to produce the three-masted carrack *(below).*

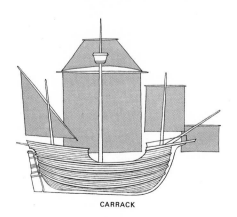

CARRACK

winner of the race home with a cargo from the Indies went the rich prize of an eager and ready market, and perhaps bonuses for all hands from happy owners. What was needed were ships that crowded on canvas, that were sharp of line and tall of mast, that could save precious time en route.

Already, American shipbuilders were working toward a design that would ultimately distinguish a bold new ship, the Yankee clipper, romantic symbol of the windship's final era. There were various reasons why they wanted faster vessels: to run from prowling European men-of-war, to do a little smuggling or privateering, or to engage in the slave trade. Chesapeake Bay shipbuilders, in particular, experimented with handy, fast, small ships and soon developed a schooner known as the "Virginia pilot boat," or the "Virginia model" which, with minor refinements, became in the 1820s the famous Baltimore clipper. (The word "clipper," American in origin, is believed to derive from "clip" in the sense of speed, as in, "to move along at a fast clip." The name was first applied to the Baltimore schooner in about 1825.)

The basic feature of these craft was a hull that sacrificed everything for speed. The ships were light rather than strong. They had great stability for carrying their clouds of canvas, but limited cargo space. These qualities were revealed in their revolutionary lines: in the sweeping rake to bow and stern, which gave greater length on deck than on the keel; in the "drag," or increased draft aft; in the steep dead rise at the midsection, making it more V- than U-shaped; in the low freeboard; in the pronounced aftward cant to the masts, which became standard with the class and with the clippers that evolved from it.

In a few brief years, the beamy, bluff-bowed ocean packet was transformed into the lovely and graceful Yankee clipper, primarily by a mating of her three masts and full ship's rig to a hull that was largely a scaled-up model of the sharp-lined, Baltimore clipper-schooner.

In an unparalleled burst of construction during the next decade or so, some 250 Yankee clippers slid off the ways of William Webb's yard in New York and Donald McKay's in Boston and those of other yards in Bath, Portsmouth, Harpswell and half a dozen other Atlantic seaport towns and joined the white-winged China tea and Gold Rush fleets.

The clipper: a fading beauty

But in the long history of the windship, the era of the full-fledged clippers was destined to be remarkably short. It began for the American ships in the 1840s, a little later for the British clippers that carried tea and Australian wool. The American clipper began to fade during the 1860s. A few years after the end of the Civil War, the Golden Spike of the completed transcontinental railway nailed her coffin lid. The British clipper lasted a few years longer. But by the mid 1870s, she too was finished and was being shuffled off to the South American guano or nitrate runs or, even more ignominiously, was set to freighting coal to the West Indies and Suez for the use of the grimy steamers that were driving her from the seas.

Nevertheless, in her heyday, when she went cracking "around the howling Horn, bound down to Singapore," she was the fastest thing that ever sailed. Clippers of the California Gold Rush fleet frequently rounded the Horn from New York to San Francisco "in two figures"— under 100 days. Such ships sometimes logged bursts of speed as high as 19 to 21 knots—fast enough to show their heels to most of today's smaller Atlantic racing yachts.

A ship for poets

It is safe to say that there never was a ship that captured the hearts of men as the clipper did. She was the white-winged epitome of speed and freedom, a thing of poetry and romance, and quite possibly every man who saw one fell a little in love with her. Some wrote sonnets to her, others, lively chanteys:

> *A Yankee ship comes down the river,*
> *Blow, boys, blow!*
> *Her masts and yards they shine like silver,*
> *Blow, my bully boys, blow!*

Although she was beautifully and lovingly made, the clipper was fatally overspecialized. This accounts for her blazing but brief career. She carried relatively little cargo. To get her best speed, she had to be driven, and to drive her, day and night, a large crew was needed. Moreover, she was always losing sails and spars, and straining her lightly built hull. When the immediate, historic pressures that created her had eased off, her day was over. She cost too much to last.

There was not much else new that could happen to the working windship. Britain, as far back as 1850, ceased building sailing men-of-war. Steam power crept in. In the 1860s, the sailing ship that carried steam for auxiliary began to disappear, to be replaced by the steamer that carried auxiliary sail. In the 1880s, Maine shipbuilders developed the fine down easter—with ample space for cargo, but only medium fast, and sparred and canvased heavily enough for driving. Though a vessel for all climes, cargoes and seasons, she too, because of her full-ship rig, was expensive to operate and unable to compete with the steamer.

This was not quite the end for the working windship. For years coastal traffic, particularly along the Atlantic seaboard, had been carried by

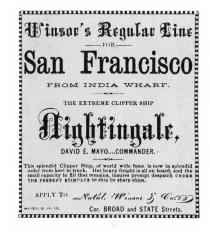

THE CLIPPER SHIP, fastest of all the great sailing vessels, is epitomized by the *Nightingale (below)*, launched in 1851. Her sleek hull and raking masts speak of a design that sacrificed all for speed. A poster of the time *(above)* advertises one of her runs from Boston to California. Lasting longer than most of her short-lived sisters, she sailed the seas for 42 years, carrying cargoes all over the world.

cargo schooners: vessels with two or more masts, all with fore-and-aft rig. They were maneuverable and dependable, although rather slow. Their chief virtue was that their simplified rig made it possible for them to be handled by much smaller crews than the complex square-riggers. Thus they hung on longer than the square-riggers, living as low-cost carriers which made their deliberate way up and down the coast. They could still be seen in Long Island Sound and Massachusetts Bay as recently as the 1920s and 1930s.

These schooners, too, had their period of specialization and gigantism. They grew larger, from two- and three-masters up to four-, five- and six-, and even one monstrous seven-master, the *Thomas W. Lawson,* built in 1902. The largest of these schooners, like the handful of square-riggers still being made, were steel-hulled by this time, with steel masts and steel rigging.

Efficient as they were, both types were doomed. Many went to the bottom in World War I and were never replaced. Others were laid up or lost at sea. A few were built in recent years, but only to serve as training ships. And in 1964, of the score or so square-riggers still afloat, 11 ghosted up the Hudson in the morning mist and anchored there for men, women and children to see and marvel at. A week later they and their silver-shining yards and masts were gone, most likely forever.

The Wind
at
Work

During the centuries that man had only sails to drive him across the oceans, he developed many kinds of rigs designed to get as much work as possible out of the fickle winds. But only in the present century has science caught up with sailing. Designers now know that there are strict laws of aerodynamics at work in a sail's operation. The application of these laws, which are much like those that keep a plane in the air, has produced sails more efficient than ancient mariners would have thought possible. Obviously, such discoveries came too late to do much good for commercial shipping: only a few reminders of another era, such as the Eastern junk, the Middle Eastern lateener and a few square-rigged training vessels, are still sailing for business. But the science of sails has been applied with great effect to the graceful yachts, large and small, that are being sailed for pleasure in increasing numbers on ponds, lakes and open waters all over the world.

SPINNAKERS FOR SPEED
Two racing yachts of the 12-meter class boil along at top speed—about 15 knots—under their huge spreads of sail. The bulging forward sails, called parachute spinnakers, are a modern development, used chiefly when the wind is behind the boat. The mainsails behind them are used all the time, and are trimmed—pulled in or let out—according to the heading a ship takes and the wind direction.

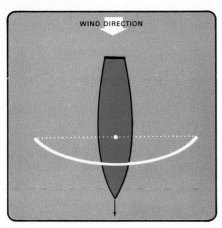

THE SIMPLEST RIG
Early seamen used the simplest form of sail—a broad surface for the wind *(arrow)* to blow against. To keep it spread, they suspended it from a "yard" *(dotted line)* hung on the mast.

Modern Sail: A Wing on Water

There is no mystery about how a ship sails in the same direction as the wind. As any child on roller skates finds out when he spreads his coat to the breeze, all that is needed for wind propulsion is a surface for the wind to push against. But how a sail moves a boat *against* the wind is not so clear. A scientific analysis of this apparent paradox was first made with the use of wind-tunnel tests in 1915 at the Massachusetts Institute of Technology. The same forces are involved that cause a wing to lift an airplane. The modern fore-and-aft sail—set along the length of a boat instead of crosswise—has the same curved shape as the upper surface of an aircraft wing. Wind flows around this airfoil to produce a "lift" that moves the boat forward *(below)*.

Yacht designers have gone so far as to try, with some success, a sail that is not only shaped like a wing, but is rigid like one. A more practical result of their scientific research is strikingly illustrated in the tall, efficient rig of the 12-meter yacht at right.

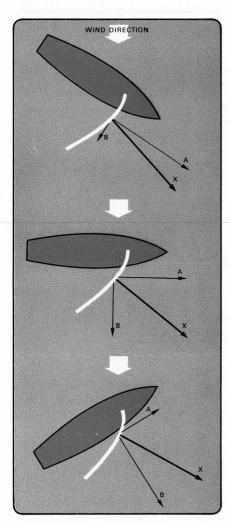

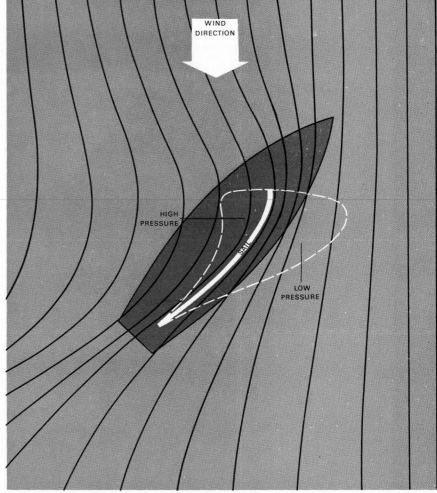

AERODYNAMICS AT WORK
These diagrams show the aerodynamics involved when a sail converts the wind's energy into forward motion. The wind's force (X) is divided by the sail into component forces, which vary as the boat changes direction. Going before the wind, most of the energy is translated into forward motion (A). As the boat turns into the wind, the forward force diminishes as more energy goes to making it heel over and drift sideways (B)—tendencies resisted by the hull's underwater shape. How a sail develops its forward push, or lift, is shown in the diagram at right. Air flowing past the outside of the sail's winglike curve has farther to travel, so it speeds up, resulting in lower air pressure in front of the sail; inside the curve the air slows and increases its pressure. The difference in pressures results in a force that moves the boat forward.

HEIGHT FOR LIFT

The *Constellation (left)*, which won the 1964 America's Cup, international yachting's most prestigious prize, exemplifies the latest development in the evolution of practical sailing rigs. Her aluminum mast is 83 feet high (15 feet longer than the boat itself); this height gives the mainsail a very long leading edge, where the strongest aerodynamic lift is generated.

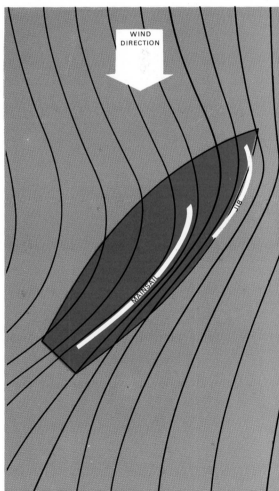

WIND
DIRECTION

MAINSAIL

JIB

A SLOT OF SAILS

The aerodynamic efficiency of the single sail illustrated on the opposite page is improved by the addition of a forward sail *(above)*, called a jib. Itself a highly efficient airfoil, the jib also creates a "slot" effect, which produces greater lift by improving the airflow over the mainsail.

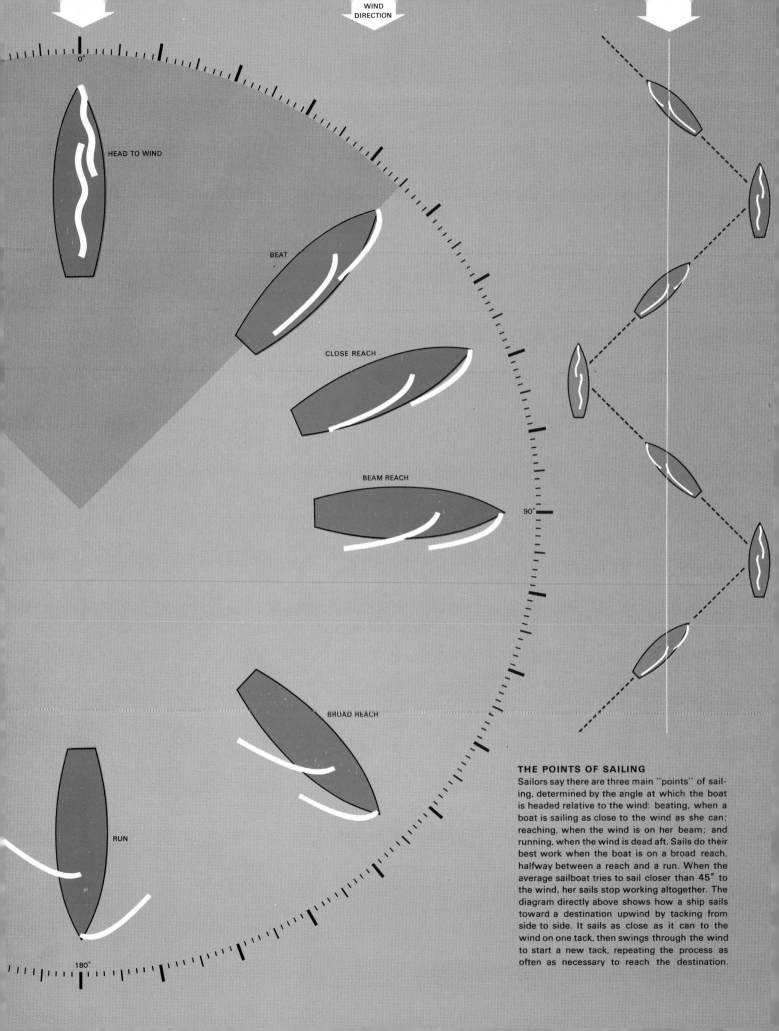

WIND
DIRECTION

0°

HEAD TO WIND

BEAT

CLOSE REACH

BEAM REACH

90°

BROAD REACH

RUN

180°

THE POINTS OF SAILING

Sailors say there are three main "points" of sailing, determined by the angle at which the boat is headed relative to the wind: beating, when a boat is sailing as close to the wind as she can; reaching, when the wind is on her beam; and running, when the wind is dead aft. Sails do their best work when the boat is on a broad reach, halfway between a reach and a run. When the average sailboat tries to sail closer than 45° to the wind, her sails stop working altogether. The diagram directly above shows how a ship sails toward a destination upwind by tacking from side to side. It sails as close as it can to the wind on one tack, then swings through the wind to start a new tack, repeating the process as often as necessary to reach the destination.

The Problem:
How to Go Upwind

Science notwithstanding, there is one thing a sailboat can never do: sail directly into the wind. As the angle between the boat's heading and the wind direction gets too fine, the air, instead of flowing smoothly over the sails, breaks away in turbulence and makes them flutter, or "luff." The sails are now doing no work and the boat can make no headway.

Apart from the unreliability of the wind itself, difficulty in moving upwind is the chief drawback of sail as a means of propulsion. To get to a destination that is in the direction the wind is coming from, a sailship must tack—zig to one side by sailing as close to the wind as possible, and then zag to the other side, gradually edging toward her goal. Square-riggers could sail no closer to the wind than about 65° before their sails lost effectiveness. This meant they had to zigzag through an arc of 130° when trying to go upwind. Beating into the wind in this manner, they often spent days covering a distance they could do in hours running before the wind.

Modern fore-and-aft rigged yachts, with their tall masts and better fitting sails made of synthetics, can sail within 45° of the wind or better. It is ironic that this close-windedness, which did not come until the end of the days of commercial sail, is now important chiefly to win yacht races.

Two boats of the same class tack upwind at close quarters in a race. Each is on a different tack, but both are moving to the same goal.

Sailing on the wind, i.e., as close as she can to the direction the wind is coming from, a two-masted junk churns along, driven by grass-mat

Wind Power in the Steam Age

Sail still provides a major source of power on the waters of a few parts of the world. On the Nile, sailors still use the lateen rig, essentially unchanged for 2,000 years. With the sail's long leading edge stiffened by a spar, much like a modern fore-and-aft rig mast, the lateen can beat within 55° of the wind to work its way upwind in a narrow river.

In the Orient, the junk (left) was developed thousands of years ago, and despite its awkward appearance is remarkably efficient. To ensure an effective airfoil shape, a junk's sails are stiffened horizontally across their entire width with flexible split-bamboo battens, a device being used by some of the most advanced modern yacht rigs. The junk is no yacht, but it is extremely seaworthy, has a large cargo capacity, and is rigged so simply that one man can take in its sails in seconds in the face of the sudden typhoons on the South China Sea. But even on junks, sail is gradually giving way to a more reliable source of power—the internal-combustion engine.

WORKING SAILS ON THE NILE

sails. Junks are used primarily in coastal waters.

Two long, lateen-rigged houseboats called dahabeahs beat up the Nile. The lateen sail is close-winded, but not easily maneuvered. In tacking, the lower end of the spar holding the sail must be dragged aft and then pulled forward again on the other side of the mast. This process requires many men and is made dangerous by the length and weight of the spar.

Last Days of a Mighty Breed

A final effort in the last days of sail to make windships profitable gave birth to monster square-riggers like the five-masted *Preussen* shown below. She was 438 feet long and 54 feet in beam—the largest sailing ship ever built (there were six- and seven-masters but they were smaller overall). With all sails set the *Preussen* could make 19 knots, a speed that compares well with that of most modern freighters. But if the wind grew too strong, men had to scurry out on the yards to gather in each sail by hand. And with no wind at all, she sat still and went nowhere.

Today few square-riggers remain. Most, like the United States Coast Guard bark *Eagle* at right, are used as naval training ships. The *Eagle* is called a bark because the sails on her aftermost mast, the mizzen, are set fore and aft. All square-riggers had some fore-and-aft sails—such as jibs and sails rigged between the masts, called staysails—for added maneuverability. Square-riggers may keep sailing for a long time: at least nine countries maintain them in the belief that experience under sail makes better officers. For most modern sailors, however, the thrill and sport of sailing is what counts, especially in moments like that shown on the following pages, when a yacht races along with all sails straining.

BIGGEST OF THEM ALL
The full-rigged ship *Preussen* was constructed in Germany in 1902 to haul nitrate from Chile to Europe. She displaced 11,150 tons fully loaded, and required a crew of 58 to handle her 60,000 square feet of sail. Each mast usually carried square sails called, from the top, skysails, royals, topgallants, upper and lower topsails, and courses; triangular jibs are forward.

TRAINING GROUND AT SEA
Driven by a following wind, the Coast Guard bark *Eagle* runs under full sail during a training voyage. The jungle of rigging is required to support her three tall masts and handle the sails.

BIRD'S-EYE VIEW OF YACHTING
The 53-foot *Malabar XIII (next page)* surges before the wind, her sails appearing to float cloudlike above her. Actually, the sails are under tremendous pressure: the nylon spinnaker is pulling with a force of at least three tons. The other sails, also made of synthetic fabrics, are, from aft, the mizzen (furled), the mizzen staysail, the main and the spinnaker staysail. →

4
The Impact of Power and Steel

IN A RARE GATHERING OF OCEAN QUEENS, EIGHT LINERS JAM NEW YORK PIERS. THE THREE BIGGEST (FROM BOTTOM) ARE "QUEEN MARY," "FRANCE" AND "UNITED STATES."

CERTAIN SHIPS have changed the world. They narrowed oceans, brought peoples and nations closer together, created a sharp dividing line between past and future. The first were sailing vessels—the Nile riverboat, the Roman merchantman, the Viking longship, Columbus' *Santa Maria*. Each, in her time, gave man a greater mastery of the sea than he had ever had before. More recently, there have been three mechanically powered ships which have had an equally profound effect upon history. All of them could have been seen in New York harbor the early part of this century.

One—the *Mauretania*, the first modern passenger liner—would undoubtedly have caught the eye of the passerby. The other two—a typical cargo ship and a typical tanker—might have been ignored. They had no individuality for there were thousands like them around the globe. To this day, a huge fleet of their kind steams the trade routes of the sea, quietly doing the world's work with efficiency and dependability.

The *Mauretania*, sister ship of the *Lusitania*, arrived in New York for the first time on November 22, 1907. Seven hundred and ninety feet long, she and her sister were the largest and fastest ships the world had ever seen. It was a foggy November dusk when the *Mauretania* steamed in from Sandy Hook, and she arrived all but unnoticed, ending her maiden voyage a little more than five days out of Liverpool. A few harbor craft saluted her, and that was all.

But with her arrival, something was quietly over, and something just as quietly had begun. A pioneering century of struggle and work, of heartbreaking trial and error had ended with a great triumph. What had begun was the 20th Century of the Atlantic Ferry, and the era of the modern powered ships. Except for refinements in detail that would come in the natural course of progress, the passenger liner of today was all there in the swift, sweeping lines, the mighty turbines, the powerful, thrusting, quadruple screws of the *Mauretania*.

Nearly everything about the *Mauretania* represented technological triumphs that summed up the full accomplishments of the Industrial Revolution. Her hull was fabricated of thousands of steel plates; her decks and topside plating were made of weight-saving, high-tensile steel. She accommodated 2,335 passengers and 812 officers and crewmen —a community of more than 3,000 souls. Her performance even today, years after she went to the breakers, still shines over the Atlantic like a star. A few months after her maiden voyage, she won the Atlantic Blue Ribbon for a record-breaking westward passage: Liverpool to New York in 4 days 20 hours 15 minutes. But it was the *Mauretania*'s complete reliability in all seas and weather, rather than her speed, that made her memorable as a working ship. Transatlantic travelers to whom time was money refused to cross on any other vessel.

Almost all ships, cargo as well as passenger, operate on fairly rigid schedules today; but for centuries there were no nautical timetables. Independence of the wind's vagaries was, however, a constantly recurring dream which began at least as far back as the days of ancient

Egypt. The mariner knew that only a mechanical means of propelling his vessel would enable him to predict, with some degree of accuracy, the time a voyage would take.

Galleys—often with slaves at the oars—were one partial answer to the problem. Galleys were used from ancient times until the early years of the 19th Century, but they were only useful in war, not in trade. To enable men to row them, a craft had to be narrow and shallow, so there was little space for cargo. Also, the limited endurance of rowers made them unfit for a long voyage. Animal power was tried, too. In a drawing of a Sixth Century A.D. Roman warship, oxen are shown yoked to capstans that, in turn, are geared to side paddle wheels. Apparently such vessels never proved practical. Centuries later, however, a horse-driven treadmill, linked to a stern wheel or side wheels, was successful. "Horse boats," as they were called, were commonly used as ferries on American rivers as late as the 1890s.

Early jet propulsion

Man-powered paddle wheels were too hard on crews, and a 17th Century scheme to drive the wheels with windmill devices proved impractical. So did two early forms of jet propulsion, one that strove to propel a boat forward by the recoil of cannons fired repeatedly off the afterdeck, and another that achieved a similar effect by drawing water in at the bow and squirting it out the stern.

The idea of propelling a boat with steam power goes back at least as far as 1690 when Denis Papin, a French inventor, physicist and mathematician suggested the possibility. Despite Papin's credentials, his proposal for a steam-driven boat was ignored. In the next century, Jonathan Hulls, an English clockmaker, published a description of a steam towboat, but it would never have remained afloat under the weight of the massive primitive engine that would have been required.

Toward the end of the 18th Century the prospects for a practical steamboat brightened. In 1783, the 130-foot *Pyroscaphe*, designed and built by the Marquis Claude de Jouffroy d'Abbans, ascended the River Saône near Lyons in France. However, the power train—reciprocating steam engine, ratchet drive and paddle wheels—was too inefficient for commercial use, and he was never able to get money to build another.

Seven years later, the American John Fitch was sufficiently confident of his steamboat to inaugurate the nation's first commercial passenger and freight service on the Delaware River. Once again, however, the handicaps were too great. The machinery needed to operate shovel-shaped stern paddles weighed too much and took up too much space to permit an economic payload.

Robert Fulton, a versatile artist and engineer, was not only aware

THE PADDLE-WHEEL SHIP appeared long before the harnessed power of steam became available. The Romans, as this medieval rendition of one of their drawings shows, found another power source when they equipped a warship with three pairs of side paddle wheels. Plodding oxen, yoked on deck to capstans, supplied the energy.

of these and other pioneering efforts; he analyzed the failures and learned from them. Fulton brought to bear on the immediate problem three assets his predecessors lacked: adequate financing (from Robert R. Livingston, American minister to France), a sound engineering background, and some solid ideas about the economic requirements of commercially successful steam navigation.

Before building his boat, Fulton experimented with various forms of screws and paddles and even anticipated William Froude's use of models in nautical research. Using a 3-foot 8-inch clockwork model, Fulton conducted tests to arrive at a hull form with low resistance to water. Later, he applied his findings to two experimental boats he built in France. Finally, on August 17, 1807, Fulton drove his flat-bottomed 140-foot vessel, the *Clermont*, clanking and smoking up the Hudson River, terrifying farmers on the riverbank and humiliating his detractors who had described the project as "Fulton's Folly."

The *Clermont* was an immediate commercial and technological success. She made the 150-mile trip from New York to Albany in 32 hours, about one third the average time of a sailing craft. The down-river return was made in 30 hours. Within a short time, she had earned back her entire initial cost of $20,000. Fulton's success was quickly copied. Within five years there were 50 steamboats in regular service on American and European inland waters.

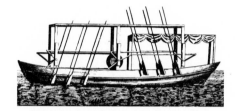

AMERICA'S FIRST POWER BOAT was a 34-foot craft designed by John Fitch in 1786. It was driven by 12 vertical oars connected to a steam engine in such a way that they alternately dipped in the water for a stroke and then were lifted out and carried forward for the next stroke. The boat worked, but its mechanism was unreliable and kept breaking down.

Inevitably, steam would now cross the Atlantic. In 1819, the full-rigged *Savannah*, one of the first sailing ships to be equipped with auxiliary steam power and side wheels, made the voyage. During the 29.5-day passage, her single-cylinder engine worked a total of some 85 hours, and consumed her entire fuel supply of 75 tons of coal and 25 cords of wood.

In following years, several other sail-steam ships crossed the Atlantic. However, skeptics derided as a lunatic's dream the idea that steam could make it alone. One might as well, said the Reverend Dionysius Lardner of Liverpool in 1835, "talk of making such a voyage from here to the moon." Three years later, two British side-wheelers, the 700-ton *Sirius* and the 1,300-ton *Great Western*, made the voyage without so much as raising a staysail.

Steps toward the modern ship

The *Clermont*, the sail-steam vessels, the ships which crossed the Atlantic exclusively with steam power—each brought man closer to the day of the truly modern ship. However, the dramatic progression from the wooden side-wheeler *Great Western* to the mighty *Mauretania* was possible only because of the confluence of three vital engineering advances made during the 19th Century. The first was metal construction, which permitted the building of larger, stronger and lighter ships than was possible with wood. Second was screw (i.e., propeller) propulsion, which used power more efficiently and gave higher speeds than paddle wheels. Finally, there was the steam turbine, which, when combined with reduction gearing and high-pressure boilers, provided an unexcelled method of converting fuel into rotary motion.

The all-metal ship actually made its appearance about a decade and a half after the *Clermont:* the *Aaron Manby,* with a hull made of iron, was launched in 1821. But the innovation was slow to gain favor with shipbuilders until its worth was proved by misadventures at sea. In 1834, a violent storm drove a number of ships ashore along the coast of England, among them, the 125-foot, all-iron *Garry Owen.* Heavy seas soon pounded some of the wooden ships to pieces and severely damaged the others. The *Garry Owen* escaped with a few dents and scrapes, and returned to port under her own steam. Twelve years later, iron won still stronger support when the *Great Britain,* the first all-metal liner, ran on the rocks in Ireland's Dundrum Bay, remained there for nearly a year without breaking up and was pulled off and restored to service.

But designers were finding other virtues in metal besides its ability to withstand punishment when a ship ran aground. Iron plates, fastened together by riveting, eliminated the defect that had plagued wooden construction of large ships since the early Egyptians: the inherent weakness of end-to-end hull-plank connections in the tension and compression stresses encountered at sea. There was a third element which weighted the scales in favor of metal. In the early 1850s, it became apparent to operators that iron ships were not only safer and lasted longer, but that they were also cheaper to build and returned a higher margin of profit than wooden vessels.

The boom in iron

A survey of windships fitted for the Far East trade, published in 1853 by James Hodgson, a Liverpool shipbuilder, disclosed that a wooden ship of 1,000 tons cost over 20 per cent more to build than an iron vessel of the same size. Furthermore, the wooden ship's capacity would be 1,500 tons of cargo, that of the iron ship of the same dimensions, 1,800 tons. These differences, plus a lower depreciation rate and less expense for insurance and interest, would bring an iron ship home from a trip to the Orient with nearly £2,300 more profit than the wooden vessel could earn. The report started an immediate boom in iron shipbuilding.

As builder of the *Great Britain,* which had demonstrated its durability on the rocky coast of Ireland, Isambard Kingdom Brunel, an English civil engineer and ship designer, did not need the survey to be convinced of the value of metal construction. On January 31, 1858, he launched the all-iron *Great Eastern,* by far the biggest, most spectacular ship the

FULTON'S FIRST STEAMBOAT was this awkward paddle-wheeler tried out in France in 1803. During its trial run in the Seine it handled well and moved against the current as fast as "a hurried pedestrian" on the shore. However, its large boiler and ponderous machinery were too heavy for the light hull that carried them.

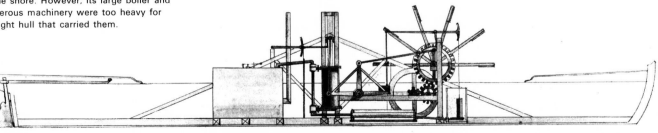

world had ever seen. She retained this distinction for almost 40 years. Nearly 700 feet long, about 85 feet in beam, almost 60 feet in depth, she was able to accommodate 4,000 passengers and carry 12,000 tons of coal—enough, so Brunel estimated, for a voyage to the Far East, out around the Cape of Good Hope, and home around the Horn.

The *Great Eastern* was historically important because she demonstrated the possibilities of metal construction for almost limitless size. However, as a working ship, she was a dismal failure. Never entered in the Orient trade for which she had been intended, she passed a few unsuccessful years on the Atlantic Ferry, was used in the laying of Atlantic cables on and off for about 10 years and ended her career as a showboat and floating amusement hall in the Mersey River.

The three decades from 1850 to 1880 were the heyday of the iron ship, but even before the launching of the *Great Eastern,* Thames builders had been experimenting with steel. It was stronger than iron, and the amount needed weighed less. By 1881, 80 per cent of all steamships under construction were being made of steel.

Ships with wheels

The development of screw propulsion, the second major innovation which led to the *Mauretania,* was going on more or less simultaneously with the adoption of metal hulls. The early steam-powered, oceangoing ships were equipped with side paddle wheels which worked well enough in relatively calm water, but it was another matter when the sea was rough. When a side-wheeler started to roll severely, for example, one wheel and then the other would come completely out of the water, wasting power and making the vessel difficult to handle.

The idea of the propeller was not new. It was first suggested—as far as is known—by Leonardo da Vinci in the 15th Century. In the years that followed, a number of men experimented unsuccessfully with screw propulsion. Finally, in 1802, Leonardo's concept was realized. The brilliant Colonel John Stevens, New Jersey lawyer-turned-inventor, constructed the first vessel to be powered by comparatively high-pressure steam and a screw propeller.

The craft was a 25-foot open boat whose machinery, for its time, was a marvel of engineering. "A cylinder of brass about eight inches in diameter and 4 inches long," Stevens wrote, "was placed horizontally in the bottom of the boat; and, by the alternate pressure of the steam on two sliding wings, an axis passing thro' its center was made to revolve. On one end of this axis, which passed through the stern of the boat, wings like those on the arms of a windmill were fixed, adjusted to the most advantageous angle for operation on the water. This constituted the whole of the machinery."

THE "CLERMONT," whose steam-driven power plant is pictured in this drawing submitted by Fulton to the U.S. Patent Office, had its triumphant first run on the Hudson River in 1807. Its improvement over its predecessor *(at left)* was mostly in a more powerful and efficient Boulton and Watt engine, and in a hull better designed to carry it.

When it perked along at full power, the little craft reached a respectable speed of four miles an hour. There was just one problem: the torque of the single screw tended to push her in circles. Stevens effected a correction in his next boat, the *Little Juliana*, built in 1804, by installing twin propellers revolving in contrary directions. However, Stevens' concepts could not be carried out on a large scale; America had neither the tools nor craftsmen to machine the parts and the engines required.

Although Stevens returned to paddle wheels for his next vessel, his work with screw propulsion was not lost. In the late 1830s, Francis P. Smith, an English inventor, and John Ericsson, the Swedish-born engineer who was later to build the Union's ironclad *Monitor*, constructed screw-propelled craft that aroused great interest in Britain. Their efficiency especially impressed I. K. Brunel who was at the time designing his *Great Britain*, the first all-iron liner. Brunel scrapped his plans for using paddle wheels and substituted a six-bladed propeller, 15.5 feet in diameter. The gamble paid off. On her maiden voyage in July 1843, the *Great Britain* made the westward passage from Liverpool to New York in 14 days and 21 hours.

Paddle wheel vs. propeller

Nevertheless, the shipping industry was slow to follow Brunel's lead. Dramatic tugs-of-war became fashionable. In 1845, for example, the British Admiralty staged one between the screw-propelled sloop-of-war *Rattler* and the paddle-wheel steamer *Alecto*. The evenly powered ships were made fast stern to stern, and given the signal to turn on full steam ahead. *Rattler's* propeller churned. *Alecto's* paddles thrashed the water. *Rattler* won, towing the other vessel stern-first at 2.5 knots.

Such performances aided the cause of screw propulsion, as did the day-after-day successful operation of ships equipped with propellers. But it was the experience of the British Navy in the Crimean War in the mid-19th Century that persuaded naval men to use only propellers on warships. Russian guns could easily disable the older type British ships by hitting their exposed paddle wheels. Soon after the war, screw propulsion was virtually universal in the up-to-date fighting ships of the world's navies. As for merchant vessels, the Cunard Line launched its last oceangoing side-wheeler, *Scotia*, in 1862. From then on, paddle-wheel craft were built only for use on coastal or inland waters.

During this period when the propeller was gradually replacing paddle wheels, the era of primitive marine steam power came to an abrupt end with the introduction of a reliable compound engine. Experimented with on land as far back as the 1780s, improved upon during the first half of the 19th Century, it was finally installed in the *Brandon* by John Elder of Glasgow in 1854.

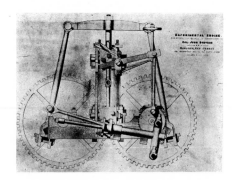

AN INGENIOUS ENGINE developed in 1804 by inventor John Stevens of Hoboken, New Jersey, powered his boat *Little Juliana*, the first vessel with two propellers. The engine's wheels, turned by the arms attached to a vertical piston, rotated the propellers in opposite directions. This eliminated the problem posed by the tendency of a single screw to push a boat in circles. However, *Little Juliana* was never a success because its boiler joints kept blowing out.

Until then, the basic design of the one-cylinder steam engine had not changed since its invention by James Watt in the 1760s. The steam expanded in the cylinder, drove the piston the full length of the stroke, then passed off through a condenser for conversion back to water. Elder's compound engine had two cylinders, one smaller than the other. The steam first entered the small cylinder, where it expanded enough to drive the piston through a stroke. Then it passed into the big cylinder, where it continued to expand, and drove a second piston. From there it went to the condenser. Thus the steam was doing double the work it had done before.

The *Brandon's* engine was an instant triumph. Knot for knot, it burned one third less coal than the single-cylinder engines of comparable vessels. Improvements quickly followed, and boosted the efficiency of later engines even higher. New boiler designs and the use of steel in place of iron made possible steadily higher pressures. By 1865, the Holt liner *Ajax*, fitted with a two-cylinder engine, was able to steam 8,500 miles from Liverpool to Mauritius in the Indian Ocean without a single stop for coal.

Pressures were further raised, and coal consumption again lowered in the 1870s with the introduction of A. C. Kirk's triple-expansion engine, in which the steam worked through three cylinders. Later, in the drive for speed, builders installed quadruple and even quintuple expansion engines in Atlantic Ferry express liners.

With the development of better, more dependable power, sail-carrying yards and masts were rapidly disappearing from the seagoing steamer. Among the first Atlantic liners to do away with them entirely were the twin-screw White Star *Teutonic* and *Majestic* launched in 1889.

By now, the need for larger and faster ships was outstripping the capabilities of the compound, or triple-expansion, engine. What was required was a wholly new type of marine engine, able to produce far greater power and transmit it with high efficiency. The answer was finally arrived at, oddly enough, through a concept over 2,000 years old.

The turbine principle

The principle of the steam turbine—rotary motion obtained directly from steam pressure—goes back to Hero of Alexandria who, in the Second or Third Century B.C., invented an engine in which steam revolved a ball. The modern version—steam driving a vaned wheel somewhat as wind does a pinwheel—was first conceived of in the 17th Century by Giovanni Branca of Loretto as a means of operating a grain-milling machine. Apparently, nothing ever came of the idea. Some 250 years after Branca had the basic concept, Sir Charles Parsons built the first successful steam turbine to power dynamos.

THE PROPELLER'S SUPERIORITY to the paddle wheel was convincingly demonstrated in 1845 when a screw *(above)* designed by the English inventor Francis Smith was installed for the first time in a British naval craft. This was the 888-ton *Rattler*, which was pitted against the 800-ton paddle-wheeled ship *Alecto* in a tug-of-war. Although both vessels had 200-horsepower engines, *Rattler* easily towed her adversary away.

In 1894, Parsons designed a marine steam turbine and installed it in his 44-ton launch, *Turbinia*. The trials were preceded by months of testing in ponds with models towed and driven with a powerful rubber-cord motor. Despite this preparation, the *Turbinia*'s initial runs were a disappointment. After trying seven different propeller designs in over 30 sea trials in which the highest logged speed was less than 20 knots, Parsons called a halt. The trouble was something that William Froude had first noted and called "cavitation." Fixed directly to one rotor shaft, the *Turbinia*'s three propellers were spinning too fast—at a speed of nearly 1,800 revolutions per minute. The blades created hollows in the water. "These cavities," noted Parsons, "contained no air, but only vapour of water, and the greater portion of the power of the engine was consumed in the formation and maintenance of these cavities instead of the propulsion of the vessel."

After further tests he came up with a design that had three shafts, each with three propellers, each driven by a slower-turning turbine. So powered, the *Turbinia* was unveiled at the British naval review at Spithead in 1897. She astounded spectators and Admiralty alike by racing down the lines at a dazzling 34.5 knots.

Power for a queen

It was only a few years after the *Turbinia*'s dramatic performance at Spithead that a special Cunard Line commission debated whether to gamble on turbine power for the new *Mauretania*. Was it practical for so large a ship? In the end, the commission voted for turbine power. Cunard's board of directors agreed. About the middle of 1905 they gave their Tyneside builders the order to lay the long steel keel of the *Mauretania*. A little more than two years later, the Atlantic Blue Ribbon was hers. It remained hers for the next 22 years.

Other changes followed the success of the turbine-powered ship. About 1920, the shift from coal to oil began. Today oil is used by more than 80 per cent of the world's steamships. Though oil is more expensive, its advantages over coal are irresistible to most operators. It can be pumped aboard swiftly, with a resultant reduction in turn-around time and with great savings in labor costs. It is easily stored in otherwise useless tank space and, most important, boosts the ship's cruising range considerably.

All this technology was not lost on the designers of other major categories of merchant ships, the cargo carrier and the oil tanker. Along with the glamorous ocean liner, they too evolved from wood and sail to steel and steam. Their sturdy, early models, differing only in dimensions and refinements from today's cargo ship and mammoth tanker, were there by the dozen in New York harbor, inconspicuous and unnoticed, the day in 1907 the *Mauretania* arrived from her maiden crossing.

What was this typical freighter like? For every inch of her 350-foot length and 50-foot beam, she was a worker with a no-nonsense air of utility to her layout and design. The bow and stern of her steel hull were high to keep waves from breaking over her decks. In heavy seas, she did, of course, ship water. There were two deckhouse structures extending across the vessel at about midships which diverted the course of the water and prevented it from having free flow over the decks and entering the engine room. The forward one contained the captain's quarters, officers' mess and navigating bridge, which was high enough to give good visibility; the other housed the machinery casing and officers' quarters. There were three watertight holds forward of the engine room and two aft. A tunnel, large enough to accommodate the propeller shaft and men who might have to inspect it, ran through the two after holds. Cargo booms radiated stiffly from the fore and aft masts, and there were steam winches for lifting goods in and out of the hatches.

As she lay at her pier, this ship was ready to carry 400,000 cubic feet of cargo—the capacity of a 150-car freight train—from anywhere to anywhere in the world at 250 miles a day. In succeeding years she and her general type changed but little. What changes there were moved in the direction of greater size and greater efficiency.

No ship, perhaps, appears more mundane and utilitarian than the bulk oil carrier, or tanker; yet no ship, in a machine-age world that runs on petroleum and petroleum products, plays a more vital role in peace or war. While sailing vessels had carried oil in barrels since the 1860s and converted steamers had transported it in bulk against their plating since the 1870s, the first oceangoing steamer designed and built as a tanker was the 300-foot, single-screw, German-owned *Glückauf*, launched in 1886. Her name, in German, means "good luck." Waterfront wags, inspired by the public distrust of carrying oil against the plating of steamers, were soon calling her *Fliegauf*, which means "blow up." She ferried oil between Europe and the United States for seven uneventful years, however, before running aground on Long Island and breaking up in 1893. Meanwhile, she proved her point. In 1885, the year before she was built, 99 per cent of American oil cargoes were carried to Europe in barrels; two decades later, 99 per cent traveled to Europe in bulk.

The three-islander tanker

The early tanker was about the same size as the early freighter but considerably different in appearance. She was called a "three-islander" because when the ship was hull down on the horizon, all that could be seen of her were three apparently unconnected superstructures—her prominent forecastle, bridge and aft deck. For reasons of safety, the tanker's engines were in the stern. To put a tunnel through the oil tanks, as

CLASSIC CARGO-SHIP DESIGN is epitomized by this plan of the S.S. *Wentworth*, built in 1914. Within her 350-foot-long steel hull, separated by watertight bulkheads, were five spacious holds with 400,000 cubic feet of cargo space. Masts, rigged with booms for loading and unloading freight through hatches on deck, were located fore and aft of the vessel's two deckhouses. Propeller-driven by the most advanced marine engine of the time, *Wentworth* could steam an average of 250 miles in one day. Freighter design during the past 50 years has varied little from this efficient and practical layout.

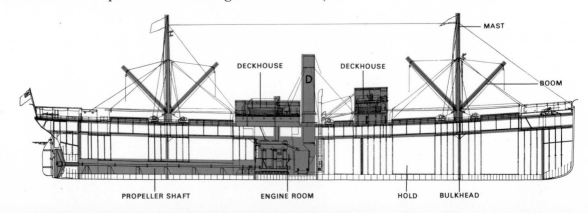

MAST

DECKHOUSE   DECKHOUSE

BOOM

PROPELLER SHAFT   ENGINE ROOM   HOLD   BULKHEAD

one was put through the holds of a freighter, would invite an explosion should there be a leakage and accumulation of gas. Over the years, there have been only minor changes in the basic design of the tanker, but the world's steadily increasing need for oil has brought about dramatic increases in her size and capacity.

The tanker *Manhattan*, largest commercial ship ever built in the United States, is a twin-screw giant, over 940 feet long. She is equipped with pumps that can discharge a full cargo of 38 million gallons of oil in less than 24 hours. When fully loaded to her maximum draft of just over 50 feet, only special, deep-water terminals can accommodate her.

For the honor of being the largest ship in the world, she is surpassed by another tanker. This is the 1,005-foot Japanese *Tokyo Maru*, launched in 1965. Although she is a little shorter than the largest ocean liners, her deadweight of 150,000 tons and her displacement of 182,500 tons make her actually a much bigger vessel than any of them. Large tankers save money. The *Manhattan*, for example, with a crew of 59, carries as much oil as six standard T-2 tankers, each of which has a crew of 41 men. How large tankers will become is impossible to say; one of 169,000 tons deadweight—considerably larger than the *Tokyo Maru*—is already on the drawing board. The only thing that seems sure is that the largest vessel afloat in the foreseeable future will almost certainly be a tanker.

A City
at
Sea

In the years since 1907, when modern ocean-liner service across the Atlantic was inaugurated by the S.S. *Lusitania* and S.S. *Mauretania*, technological improvements have affected every phase of passenger-ship design. The 1,035-foot-long S.S. *France*, in service since 1962, incorporates scientific advances in the design of the hull, machinery and accommodations that would have astonished the *Mauretania*'s builders. Propelled by one of the most efficient marine-propulsion systems ever devised and guided largely by automatic controls, the ship makes the run from New York to Le Havre in only five days—far less time than it takes to sample all its facilities. This 66,000-gross-ton vessel is also a self-sufficient hotel which can lodge more people—2,044 passengers and 1,112 crewmen—than the Waldorf-Astoria. The pride of the French merchant marine is both a pleasure palace and a triumph of 20th Century marine engineering.

ELEGANCE AND POWER
Cutting through calm waters, the S.S. *France* makes a steady 33 knots—about 38 miles per hour—as it heads toward New York. The vessel's glistening finish is constantly maintained by retouching, both at sea and during its fortnightly visits to its home port of Le Havre. The ship's entire bottom is scraped clean and given a new coat of red paint twice each year in dry dock.

A GUIDED TOUR OF THE "FRANCE"

1 RUDDER
2 HYDRAULIC STEERING MECHANISM
3 PROPELLERS
4 TOURIST-CLASS SWIMMING POOL
5 TOURIST-CLASS CABINS
6 CREW'S QUARTERS
7 TOURIST-CLASS MAIN LOUNGE
8 SQUASH COURT
9 FIRST-CLASS SALON
10 TOURIST-CLASS DINING ROOM
11 REDUCTION GEAR
12 FRESH-WATER DISTILLERS
13 BOILERS
14 PROPELLER SHAFTS
15 FIRST-CLASS CABINS

16 FIRST-CLASS MAIN LOUNGE
17 KITCHEN
18 REFRIGERATED ROOMS
19 AFT STABILIZER FIN
20 FUEL-STORAGE BUNKER
21 WINE CELLAR
22 FIRST-CLASS SWIMMING POOL
23 FIRST-CLASS DINING ROOM
24 DELUXE SUITE
25 MOVIE THEATER
26 CHAPEL
27 PLAYROOM
28 TURBINES
29 HOSPITAL
30 LIFEBOATS

31 AIR-CONDITIONING MACHINERY
32 CAPTAIN'S QUARTERS
33 CHART ROOM
34 BRIDGE
35 FREIGHT HOLD
36 GARAGES
37 CARGO HATCHES
38 ANCHOR-WINDLASS ROOM
39 ANCHORS
40 WATER LINE
41 STABILIZING BILGE KEEL
42 STABILIZER MECHANISM
43 SMOKE FILTER
44 FUNNEL AILERONS
45 RADAR MAST

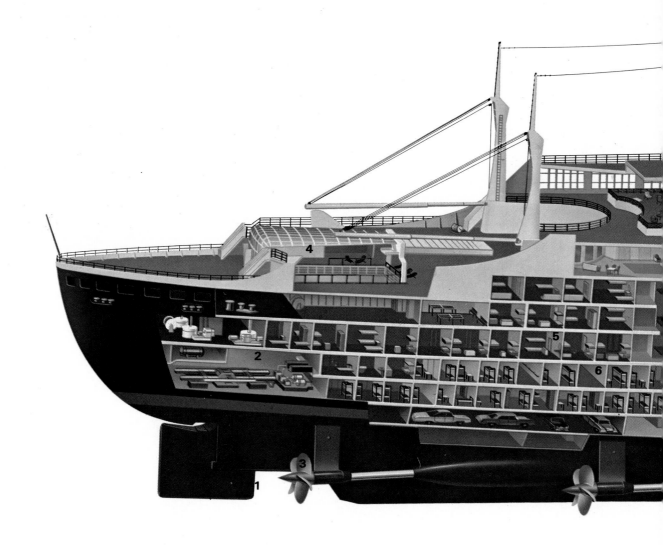

Using Every Inch of Space

The interior of the *France*'s hull is divided into thousands of compartments—ranging from a cramped tool room to a tourist lounge bigger than six tennis courts. The engine rooms *(orange)* are located as low in the ship as possible, well insulated from recreation areas and passenger quarters *(5, 15, 24)*. Storage areas, which hold enough supplies to support the ship's population for 10 days, include 18 refrigerator rooms *(18)* set at different temperatures for different foods such as cheese, meat and potatoes. Various fuel compartments *(20)* store 10,000 tons of oil. There is even storage space for 100 automobiles *(36)*.

About 30 miles of air-conditioning ducts cool all interior areas and 18,-000 miles of wiring carry electricity to every compartment. Two pairs of gyroscope-controlled stabilizing fins *(19)* reduce roll to a minimum.

Most of the superstructure and some other parts of the hull are aluminum. Such weight-saving, a sleeker hull shape and an improved propulsion system make the *France* far more efficient than earlier ships like the S.S. *Normandie*, built in 1935. When *France* is turning out 160,000 horsepower, *Normandie*'s top, she goes five knots faster than her predecessor and burns 40 per cent less fuel.

At sundown, officers of the *France* take the evening watch on the bridge. Rising behind are the funnels with winglike extensions that blow

engine smoke and soot to the side so it does not fall on the decks. This innovation helps make the *France* one of the cleanest ships afloat.

George V Kelvin

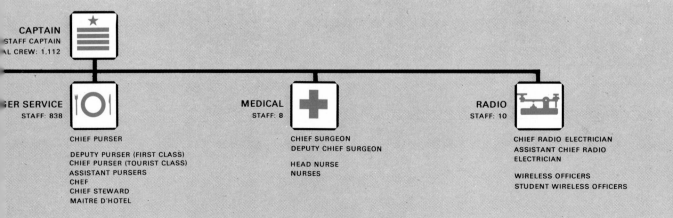

THE CHAIN OF COMMAND

Matching the economical utilization of the ship's hull and deck space is the efficient organization of her crew. Although the captain's command of his ship is as absolute as in simpler times, a modern ocean liner is so complex that he delegates most operational responsibilities along the lines shown in the chart at right. The head of each service makes daily reports to the captain, who thus maintains executive control over all of the ship's vital functions. Should the necessity arise, three other officers on the ship are fully licensed to take command.

BRIDGE
STAFF: 93

SECOND CAPTAIN (CHIEF MATE)
DEPUTY SECOND CAPTAIN

NAVIGATION OFFICER
LIEUTENANTS
STUDENT OFFICERS

ENGINEERING
STAFF: 163

CHIEF ENGINEER
ASSISTANT CHIEF ENGINEER

SECOND ENGINEERS
CHIEF ELECTRICIAN
ASSISTANT CHIEF ELECTRICIAN
STUDENT OFFICERS
ASSISTANT FOR AIR CONDITIONING

PASSEN

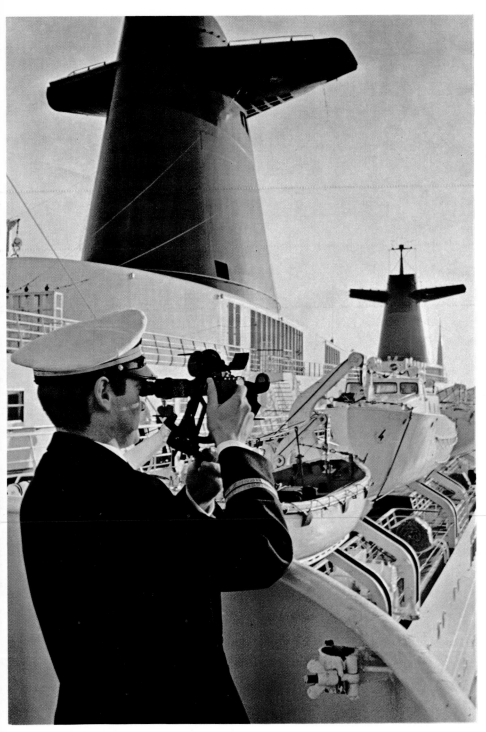

VIEW FROM THE BRIDGE
Captain Joseph Ropars surveys the sea from the bridge. Behind him a sailor mans the wheel: he actually steers only during maneuvers, in very bad weather or if the automatic pilot should fail.

SHOOTING THE SUN
Sighting through a sextant, a navigation officer determines the angle of the sun above the horizon. When applied to navigational tables and combined with the results of other sights, this information will enable him to determine the ship's position. Celestial navigation provides a dependable check against possible failure of the vessel's electronic navigation instruments.

POWER STEERING
Deep in the ship's stern a mechanic adjusts the top of the spindle from which the vessel's rudder is suspended 20 feet underneath. Two pairs of shiny hydraulic pistons could swing the 74-ton rudder through an arc of 70° in 30 seconds even if the ship were moving at top speed.

Getting the "France" from Port to Port

In navigating the S.S. *France* along a 3,250-mile invisible highway across the North Atlantic, the ship's officers still use many of the techniques that mariners have employed for centuries. But the *France* is also equipped with an intricate electronic navigational system that actually does most of the work of guiding the ship at sea.

The core of the steering system is an automatic pilot, teamed with a highly accurate gyroscopic compass which is linked to a hydraulic rudder mechanism (*below*). Once the automatic pilot is set with a course to steer, it instantly responds to any deviation in the ship's heading caused by wind and waves, and relays corrective orders to the rudder.

As the vessel cruises under automatic controls, other instruments insure its safe progress: an electric log keeps a running record of speed and course; two ultrasonic devices measure the sea's depth; a Decca Navigation Aid picks up radio signals from shore stations and instantly plots the ship's location; radar beams sweep a 40-mile circle in ceaseless survey of the sea even in darkness or fog. With this impressive battery of instruments in operation, the *France*, after five days of steaming, almost always reaches its destination within minutes of its planned time of arrival.

PILOT AT WORK
The *France*'s wake, weaving back toward the horizon, is the visible result of commands from the automatic pilot to the rudder as it makes constant corrections in the vessel's heading.

The Mighty Power Plant

The *France*'s driving force originates in her eight three-story-high boilers which generate steam at 1,042° F and pressures of about 1,000 pounds per square inch. This violent energy is channeled into four whirling turbines which, through reduction gears, turn the four propeller shafts. The system can turn out 175,000 horsepower, a little more than that produced by 29 smaller, less efficient boilers on the old *Normandie*. The *France*'s engines weigh 3,000 tons less than the *Normandie*'s, and they burn about 2,500 gallons less fuel every hour.

This awesome aggregate of machinery is housed in two gleaming but clamorous engine rooms under the constant surveillance of the engineering crew. In the unlikely event that one engine room were to be put out of commission, the other could still push the vessel at 23 knots, almost two thirds of its full speed.

Besides propulsion, the *France*'s machinery provides energy for a variety of functions: producing 13,500 kilowatts of electricity to light, heat and air-condition the vessel, generating current for all the vital navigation, guidance and communications systems—including 1,300 telephones —and distilling 350,000 gallons of fresh water from the sea every day.

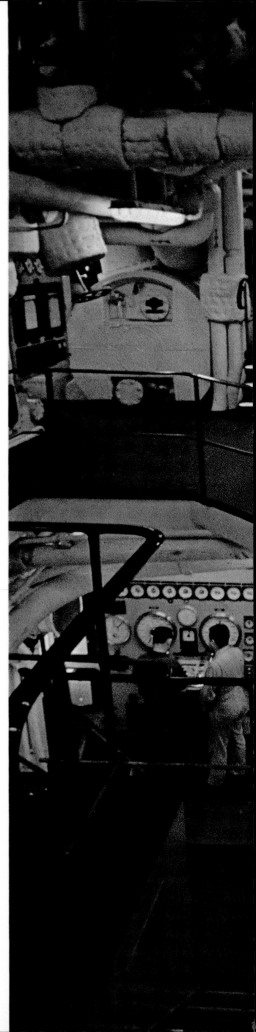

TURNING THE SCREWS

One of two 390-foot propeller shafts from the forward engine room stretches down its "alley" toward the ship's stern. Protected by a coat of paint and held in alignment by 13 bearings, the shaft turns a 28-ton propeller at 166 rpm when the ship is traveling at top speed—35.2 knots. The shaft, made up of nine sections of forged steel 23 inches thick, weighs 58 tons.

TENDING A NOISY GIANT

Mechanics working on both tiers of one of the *France*'s duplex engine rooms *(right)* keep an eye on their power plant. They normally get orders from the bridge on electrically controlled indicators. Intense noise makes telephone exchanges possible only from soundproof booths.

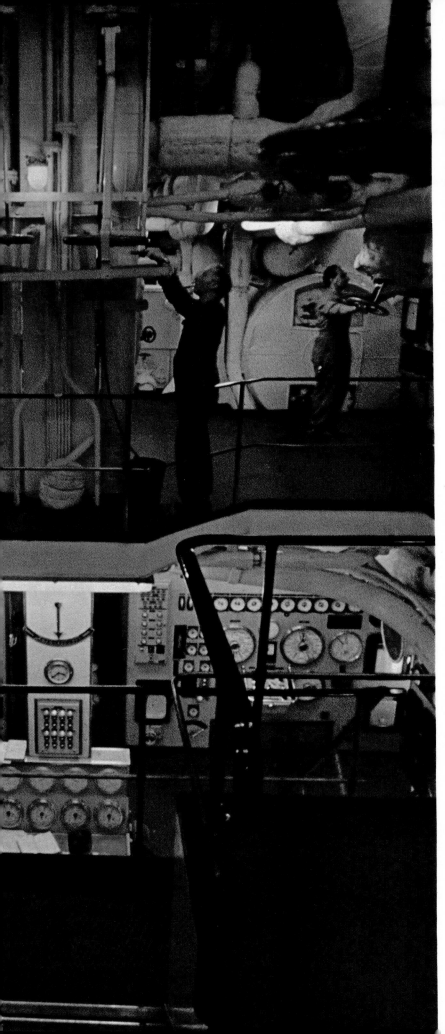

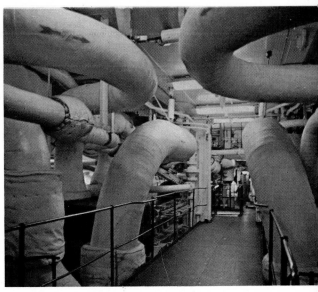

A LABYRINTH OF TUBES
Wrapped in asbestos shielding, a tangle of pipes winds through one of the engine rooms carrying steam, fuel and water. The red arrow indicates a steam pipe and shows direction of flow.

MONITORING AN INFERNO
Peering through a protectively tinted window, a boilertender checks the 3,275° F flame of a burner heating one of the vessel's eight boilers. Each boiler has six burners, similar in principle to those in home furnaces: altogether, the burners consume up to 41 tons of fuel oil an hour.

Keeping Safe at Sea

The *France* was designed with as much emphasis on safety and the passengers' security as on speed. The ship has double-hull construction for nearly half its length and is subdivided into 15 watertight compartments; if the hull were punctured, 59 steel doors would clang shut at the touch of a button to prevent general flooding. Other devices guard against fire. For example, 430 heat sensors will automatically detect any sudden rise in temperature and report instantly to the vessel's central security office. The ship has practically no wood, and even the art works have been fireproofed.

Virtually unsinkable, totally fireproof, crammed with enough radio gear to beam seven communications to the shore at once and furnished with a modern, 23-bed hospital—as well as a morgue—*France* is equipped to cope with any emergency at sea.

PATTERNS OF SECURITY

An officer at the ship's safety console keeps in constant telephone communication with the ship's fire-fighting stations. Attended 24 hours a day, the control board registers the whereabouts of patrolling security guards on all 12 decks *(right panel),* indicates the position of fire doors, controls fire-fighting equipment and instantly reports any outbreak *(left panel).*

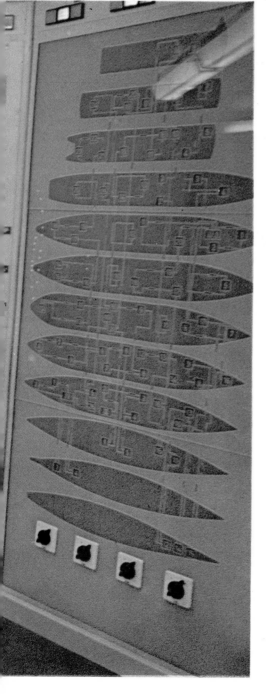

THE VITAL LINK TO LAND

In the radio room *(above)* directly behind the bridge, radio officers man the elaborate communications system by which the *France* can get in touch instantly with any part of the world. The radio staff also provides the ship's daily paper with bulletins via teletypewriter.

READY FOR ANYTHING

Removing steel splinters from a seaman's hand, one of the ship's two doctors works with a nurse in the well-equipped hospital which contains operating and delivery rooms and an isolation ward. The medical staff is also ready to tend colds and dispense pills for seasickness.

DINING FIRST CLASS

Dinner in the 410-seat first-class dining room —where formal dress is traditional—is an unhurried affair. On gala evenings the captain usually joins passengers at dinner, presides over his table and officiates at a formal dance which sometimes continues throughout the night.

A BUSTLING, ORDERLY KITCHEN

Beneath rows of white cups, some of the ship's 150 waiters race to pick up orders from the kitchen's service counters. The cups, hung from the ceiling to conserve space, are part of a table service that includes 30,000 plates, 10 tons of silverware and 275,000 pieces of table linen.

Leisurely Days,
Gracious Evenings

All the mechanical functions of the *France* are ultimately directed toward supporting the luxurious life of its passengers. No less than three quarters of the crew are employed in hotel services, including stewards, maids, launderers and bootblacks. In the grand manner of the finest European hotels, the ratio of servers to the served is better than 1 to 3.

The *France* boasts a branch of a Paris department store, telephones in every room, two indoor swimming pools, bilingual secretaries, kennels for dogs, sitters for babies and a 664-seat movie theater—the largest theater afloat. The ship even offers thalassotherapy, an exotic form of physical therapy involving hot algae baths, massages and cold showers.

But to many passengers the chief luxury of the *France* is the astonishing size and variety of the ship's cuisine. More than 150 cooks can convert the 75 tons of raw food taken on for each round-trip voyage into as many as 9,000 meals every day. Despite the efficiency of the gleaming production-line kitchens, traditional French standards are maintained.

A WELL-STOCKED CELLAR
The ship's chief *sommelier,* or wine steward, shown inspecting a vintage Bordeaux wine, is in charge of more than 35,000 bottles of wines and liquors, including 60 different champagnes.

Keeping Up with the World

Ocean liners are as beautiful as ever, though they are not as ornate as they once were. The decorative gilt and gewgaws, the Louis XVI settees, velvet draperies and crystal chandeliers have given way to plastic, aluminum and stainless steel. Still, the romance of a sea voyage is strong—not only for the well-to-do, but for the tourist-class travelers who now make up two thirds or more of most passenger lists.

Only by being modernized from keel to radar mast and by applying the most efficient technology in design and machinery can the ocean liner hope to compete in an era when more than 80 per cent of transoceanic traffic is carried by airplane. Even the schedules have been modernized: to keep up with the times, the *France* leaves its cold North Atlantic run every winter and makes holiday cruises to the Caribbean, Africa and the Mediterranean.

Not only France, but Italy and Britain have launched, or are planning, new liners for the transatlantic and cruise trade. These new ships are proving that the luxury of leisure can hold its own in an age of speed.

SLIPPING INTO PORT
Its trim shape outlined against still waters, the *France* slowly steams into New York harbor at dawn. Land-bound only long enough to restock and take on new passengers, the ship will catch a high tide on the following day and begin its 3,250-mile journey once again.

5

The
Cargo
Carriers

STANDARDIZED CONTAINERS, A TIME-SAVING INNOVATION IN SEA TRANSPORT, ARE LOADED ONTO A WAITING SHIP.

IN AN ERA when cargo ships, tankers and passenger liners follow schedules as routinely as suburban letter carriers and milkmen, reliable, orderly waterborne commerce is accepted as a matter of course. To the 19th Century mind, however, the feat seemed a triumph of cosmic proportions. "When its errands are noble and adequate," wrote Ralph Waldo Emerson, "a steamship bridging the Atlantic between Old and New England and arriving at its ports with the punctuality of a planet, is a step of man into harmony with nature."

Men of Emerson's day had good reason to look with awe upon the emergence of an oceangoing vessel that operated with timetable punctuality. The ship was rapidly bringing about radical and profound changes in the lives of men on every part of the globe and creating a heretofore undreamed-of interdependence among the family of nations. "For good or ill," wrote Philip B. Fleming, former Maritime Commissioner, "civilization became the child of the steamship." Civilization's reliance upon the ship has grown steadily.

Largely because of ships, factories operate, people are fed, men are able to sell the products of their labor, farmers have markets for what they grow, miners and oil drillers can supply users, travelers can journey around the world luxuriously, if not as rapidly as by air. Today there are some 21,500 powered ships of 1,000 or more gross tons—passenger liners, freighters and tankers—carrying on this vital global commerce.

Even the United States, the most highly industrialized, most nearly self-sufficient nation on earth, is reliant to a great degree upon the steady workhorse ships that ply between the ports of the world. Exports are, of course, important to the economic health of the country; in 1964 sales of ship-carried goods abroad totaled $17 billion. But imports, too, are of enormous consequence, not only in the maintenance of the standard of living and high-level production, but also to national defense.

In 1964 waterborne imports reached a record high of more than 400 million tons, with a collective price tag of more than $13 billion. Such luxuries as Swiss watches, Russian furs, Scotch whiskey, Italian shoes, Danish furniture and French wines were a part of the overseas purchases, but only a minor part. The major imports were vast quantities of essential raw materials. Certain of them the U.S. lacks entirely; the domestic supply of others is not adequate to meet the demand. In some instances, conservation of native resources is the reason for importing. A century of rapid industrialization and two World Wars have made deep inroads into the nation's natural wealth.

In this category of imports in 1964 were almost 450 million barrels of crude oil; more than 40 million tons of iron ore (one third the national consumption); more than 10 million tons of bauxite (about 85 per cent of the domestic aluminum industry's total requirements) as well as 80 to 100 per cent of all the tin, chromite and manganese used in the production of rockets, jet planes and other items that have become an intrinsic part of the national life.

Continental Europe and Great Britain are even more dependent upon outside sources for fuel, raw materials and many kinds of food, and a high percentage of these goods comes from the United States. The reciprocal transport between the two great industrial centers creates the world's busiest trade routes in the North Atlantic. A bridge of ships on these sea-lanes is as vital in peacetime as it was in the two World Wars.

The Atlantic Ferry and the operation of ships on a dependable schedule—the basis of today's complex international trade—began only a century or so ago with the launching of the first regularly scheduled, steam-driven Cunarder, the *Britannia*. The bullyboys of the sailing packets could leave Liverpool on the dot, and crack on all the canvas the spars would carry, but no one ever knew whether the ship would arrive in New York on time, or five to 10 days later. In 1866, the clipper *Serica* made it home to London from Foochow in 99 days; in 1867, she took 120.

The steamship, capable of arriving on schedule or close to it despite head winds, rough seas and contrary tides, imposed order on waterborne commerce. Such punctuality represented a gain, not only in dependability, but also in carrying capacity: more voyages meant more cargo. It has been estimated that while British-registered merchant marine tonnage increased only 150 per cent between 1850 and 1900, the annual carrying power rose 700 per cent.

The momentous innovations brought about by steam—mainly a dependable schedule and increased carrying power—opened a new era in world trade and international relations. There was an expansion of industrialized cities and nations. Now, for the first time, factories had a reliable, day-to-day inflow of raw materials from all parts of the globe, and the means of shipping an even outflow of finished products. Regions or even entire nations could specialize in the kinds of production best suited to them, and rely on steady supplies of other goods that could be produced elsewhere more economically.

New ports for new ships

The shoreside facilities had to remain abreast of these developments. New, modernized ports brought freight cars and canal boats to the pier to connect with the seagoing ships. In such ports as New York, "finger" piers, extending at right angles from the shore, made possible the swift and efficient transfer of cargoes between ships and the river barges and lighters that linked the Manhattan waterfront with the continental freight-line terminals across the Hudson in New Jersey. Little by little, every inland city, village and farm became, through the seagoing ship, the neighbor of every other throughout the world.

Since the end of World War II a new revolution has been taking place in shipping. As international trade grows and increased competition brings demands for speedier, less expensive delivery, there is progressively greater need for (1) fast, direct linkage between inland shipping points on one continent and inland destinations on another; and (2) means of transporting more products economically in bulk. The designs of the ships themselves are reflecting the new requirements. An era of specialized vessels is underway.

Some of the most dramatic changes are found in tankers, largely because of the growing number of products being carried in bulk. Until comparatively recently, tankers carried petroleum almost exclusively. Today, nearly everything liquid or even semiliquid seems to be going to sea. Orange juice, tallow, molasses, vegetable oils and cleaning fluids, among many other products, are being shipped in specialized tankers.

A big West Coast lumber and paper company uses a specially designed tanker to carry semiliquid wood pulp from the manufacturer's storage areas to its coastal or river-based paper mills. Formerly the pulp was processed into dry sheets, bundled, shipped, and then at its destination reliquefied for use in the manufacture of paper. Now it is piped aboard the tanker in a few hours. At the paper mill, the pulp is pumped directly into shoreside tanks—a faster, cheaper, more efficient operation.

Because the chemical composition of a container often causes changes in a given liquid, and the liquid may corrode the container, the internal tanks of a modern tanker may be made of, or lined with, a special material which will not affect the specific cargo the ship is designed to carry. Glycerin, for example, is transported in a tank lined with nickel.

The floating wine cellar

United Vintners of California ship nearly 2.5 million gallons of San Joaquin Valley wine in bulk from California to New Jersey via the Panama Canal in the 26 huge, stainless-steel vats of the S.S. *Angelo Petri*, known as the "floating wine cellar." Wing ballast tanks are ordinarily filled with water to add weight when a ship has a light cargo. On the *Angelo Petri*, some of these tanks have enameled interiors to carry an additional payload of 500,000 gallons of vegetable oils on the west-east passage. On the return voyage, the tanker transports sugar in solution with water, potable alcohol and other liquid cargoes which can travel unchanged in the ship's special linings. The *Angelo Petri*, which has largely supplanted rail tank cars in the company's bulk shipment of wine, has meant lower costs and reduction of the wine's exposure to air (and thus an improvement in its flavor).

The problem of special linings was not the only one that the designers of modern tankers had to solve. Certain products must be kept at extremely low temperature during transportation; others must be under pressure; still others require great heat. Modern tankers have successfully met all of these needs.

EVOLUTION OF CARGO SHIPS, in terms of speed and capacity, is plotted on the chart below, beginning with the clipper ship of 1850. The dry-cargo-carrying freighter has increased in speed to a fast 20 knots, but has changed little in freight capacity *(light gray line)*. The tanker came later; because huge quantities of oil can be handled much faster than dry cargo, tankers *(dark gray line)* have developed into mammoth carriers which can haul more than seven times the tonnage of the biggest freighters.

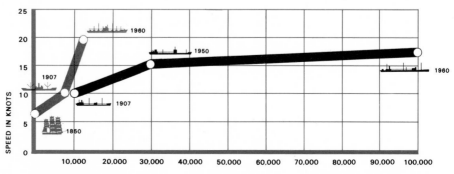

Because of specialized tankers, Trinidad now has a multimillion-dollar industry which manufactures ammonia from the island's rich supply of natural gas. Ammonia must be transported either at a low temperature or under pressure. Each of the two tankers built for W. R. Grace and Company is a floating refrigerator which can carry 9,000 tons of liquid ammonia at −28° F. directly from Trinidad to worldwide markets. Until the development of such a ship, the island's potential as a producer of a product in great demand—especially in the making of nitrogenous fertilizer—could not be realized.

New tankers carry hot cargo, too. Not long ago, Gulf Coast producers of sulfur, used in many manufacturing processes, mined it in molten form at 300° F., then cooled and solidified it and shipped it dry. At the other end, most consumers, before using the sulfur, had to melt it back into liquid form. Today tankers take aboard the liquid sulfur, carry it in specially insulated, steam-heated tanks at 270° F., and discharge it directly into heated storage tanks in the consumer's home port. In the ship's hold are specially designed tanks with supports which permit the hot containers to expand without affecting the hull of the vessel.

Gas for British stoves

Because Great Britain has almost no natural gas, some 500 trillion cubic feet of this fuel must be manufactured annually from coal. The process is expensive. Now, thanks to an experimental tanker, the *Methane Pioneer,* designed to carry liquefied natural gas under pressure and at extremely low temperature, many British homes are being heated, and British meals prepared, with gas from the oil fields of Algeria—and at an estimated cost about two thirds that being paid for the manufactured product.

To transport natural gas economically, it must first be converted to a liquid state by reducing its temperature to −260° F. before piping it aboard the tanker, where it is kept under pressure. Because ordinary steel becomes brittle at such a low temperature, the ship has welded aluminum tanks, each jacketed in 12 inches of laminated balsa wood for insulation, and the entire unit enclosed in steel. There are five such containers—each 40 feet long, 30 feet wide and 30 feet deep—built into the tanker. These containers can hold evaporation of the liquid gas down to 0.5 per cent during a three-week voyage.

When the liquefied gas arrives in England, it is transferred to storage tanks where it is reconverted to a gaseous state. One barrel of liquid gas yields about 3,500 cubic feet of natural gas.

Like the tanker, the cargo vessel is being radically affected by the growing requirements of international trade. Bulk shipment of dry cargoes is also increasing rapidly. Until a few decades ago only coal, ores and grain were shipped in bulk. Today, specially designed ships carry sugar, fertilizers, salt, powdered detergents and dozens of other products. Such a specialized freighter usually has the engine room in the stern, and almost the entire hull is divided into a series of huge holds extending from the top deck to the bottom of the ship. Fast conveyor belts, powerful pumps or similar devices load and unload the cargo.

An equally important innovation is the container-ship, the first all-new category of oceangoing peacetime craft since the introduction of the tanker. This vessel provides the waterborne relay in "containerization"—the movement of nonbulk goods from sender to consignee in standardized, metal receptacles which can be readily transferred from one type of carrier to another. The system makes it possible for goods to be packed in a container at the point of origin and delivered to their destination with no intermediary handling of the contents. Enormous savings in transportation costs can result.

How does containerization work? Assume a machine-tool company in Cincinnati is shipping lathes to Puerto Rico. At the plant, the lathes are securely packed in an aluminum container measuring 8 by 8½ by 35 feet, the size of a standard truck trailer, and then lifted onto the trailer bed. The truck takes the box to the railroad yards, where it is placed upon a flatcar especially built to transport containers of that size. It now travels by rail to Jacksonville, is again placed on the bed of a truck and is hauled to the pier where a container-ship is loading. Here a ship-mounted gantry crane lifts the container off the truck chassis, swings it aboard and lowers it into the hold.

The container-ship is an entirely new kind of vessel. She has no interior decks. Her engine room is in the stern and her hull is simply an enormous warehouse about 500 feet long, subdivided into "cells" by vertical guides or racks, which guide the containers as they are lowered into the ship and hold them fast in rough weather. When the holds are full, other containers are lashed to the deck. Because the containers are metal and well sealed, the contents will not be damaged by rain or spray from the sea.

When the container-ship arrives in Puerto Rico, a reverse loading process takes place. Cranes place the containers directly on the truck bed, which transports them to the ultimate destination. The box of lathes, packed in Cincinnati, arrives at the purchaser's plant without ever having been opened en route.

Old methods and high costs

Aside from the smooth, efficient flow made possible by containerization, however, the handling of general cargo remains, in this era of mechanization, strangely archaic. Once a shipper's merchandise is in the hold and on the high seas, he pays less freight per ton-mile than he would for any other method of transportation in the world. But the expense of moving goods in and out of the ship and a few hundred feet along piers at each end of the crossing may well cost him as much as it does to move the cargo over 3,000 miles of ocean.

The reasons for high dockside costs are many. Articles routinely transported in corrugated cartons on land must be specially crated for travel in ships. In a port as busy as New York, dozens of firms specialize in export packing alone. Once crated, the goods are usually stored in a warehouse near the pier. There is individual handling in each instance.

When it is time for shipboard loading, the crates are moved once more, from storage area to shipside. The loading gang hoists them aboard in a cargo sling, using a system little changed since the turn of the century. Down below, in the open holds, longshoremen stow the crates in the ship's hold much as they did in the days of the California clippers. Such antiquated cargo-handling methods cause even the most modern non-container cargo ship to spend more than half the year tied up at the pier—a multimillion-dollar investment that is productively employed for less than half its life.

Expenses skyrocket under such a system. A recent paper by John L. Eyre, an expert on water transport, analyzed costs for a number of overseas shipments from inland point of departure to inland point of destination and reported, for example, that it cost about $2,500 to move 15 tons of medical and pharmaceutical supplies from Chicago to Nancy, France. Of this amount, 53 per cent went for costs in the two terminal seaports. Handling charges in the U.S. port were three times as high as those in France.

Containerization may well help to reverse this trend of rising costs. The savings in money and time on the pier alone are enormous. On most American piers, it costs about $3.90 per ton to load cargo into a ship's hold by the routine, old-fashioned method of handling. Containerized cargo can be put on board for 35 to 40 cents per ton. It takes a 20-man gang an hour to load about 17 tons; some 360 containerized tons can be stowed in the same period by a smaller number of men. Damage claims on hand-loaded shipments often run 30 cents or more per ton. With containers, the claims average 1.6 cents per ton, and pilferage losses are reduced from millions of dollars a year to almost nothing.

Because of these advantages, containerization has made rapid strides since World War II, when the U.S. Navy pioneered the concept by strapping many packages to a single pallet, or wooden tray. Somewhat later, the U.S. Army began using compact metal receptacles, and instituted the first worldwide system of containerized cargo.

Since the 1950s, when it entered civilian cargo handling, containerization has gained favor in many parts of the world and especially in the United States in coastal and intercoastal shipping, and between the mainland and Hawaii, Alaska and Puerto Rico.

Problems with a big box

A number of problems remain to be solved, however. Because both land and sea transportation use the container, for example, there are questions about who should own and maintain it. Also, the customs bureaus of various nations are undecided about where the container should be opened for inspection. Normally, cargoes are examined at the port of entry. If this is done with containerized goods, many of the advantages of the system are lost. However, to have a customs man at the ultimate destination of every container also poses difficulties.

Lack of standardization of size of containers is another obstacle which must be cleared. Lengths, for example, vary from 10 feet or less to 35 feet. Therefore, a ship with racks designed to handle one size usually cannot take another. The future trend may be toward 20- and 40-foot-long, standard-sized boxes, some of which may be specialized. One proposed specialized container would be 40 feet long, and fitted with retractable ramps for carrying automobiles or with collapsible rubber tanks for carrying liquid cargo. With tanks removed and ramps folded back against floor and ceiling, the receptacle could hold dry cargo.

The radical changes in the ways of handling cargo, the new ships and the demands of commerce have inevitably brought about innovations in many ports and terminal facilities. One of the most advanced of such installations was constructed at Elizabeth, New Jersey, by Sea-Land Service, Inc., which is engaged in the shipment of trailer-containers between the continental United States, Alaska and Puerto Rico, and between mainland ports. All aspects of the facilities are aimed at an even, unimpeded flow of traffic through the port.

Beltline loading at the pier

A trailer truck enters the port area at a precisely assigned time and is directed to one of the three incoming lanes which pass by one side of the truck-operations office. The lanes are equipped with electronic scales which weigh the load and transmit the information to the ship-loading area. Also in each lane is a pneumatic tube which whisks pertinent papers about the cargo to the proper office.

The lanes now lead to marine operations. There is berthing space for four container-ships in this section of the port, and as each truck comes to a stop at its assigned place, a crane aboard the vessel lifts the trailer from the truck bed and places it in the hold. Following the same lane, the truck then leaves the port. With this system, a container-ship has a turn-around time—the unloading and loading period—of 12 hours, compared with the conventional freighter's three to four days.

New port facilities are also being constructed for tankers. The first large tankers, because of their enormous draft, were always forced to discharge part of their cargoes to smaller vessels while at anchor in deep water. When their draft had been sufficiently reduced, they proceeded to their terminals. But within only a few years, progressive ports around the world—San Diego, Milford Haven, Rotterdam—have built deep-water piers where supertankers can tie up and discharge or take on cargo through pipelines to shoreside storage tanks. To facilitate the loading of tankers at oil fields in Middle and Far Eastern coastal regions where no adequate harbors exist, oil-company engineers have constructed excellent offshore loading facilities—such as a submarine pipeline on the island of Borneo extending from storage tanks on shore to a mooring buoy hundreds of yards from the beach. The empty tanker simply anchors near the buoy, takes aboard hoses from the end of the underwater

A RARE DOCKSIDE CRANE, used in the French port of Dunkirk in the 18th Century, was a timesaver that did not come into widespread use until the Industrial Revolution in the 19th Century. This machine could be wheeled to the side of the ship, where its two hoists, raised and lowered by a hand crank, could be operated at the same time.

pipeline, connects them to her intake valves, and the cargo is pumped from the shore into her tanks. If the waters become rough during the operation, the ship disconnects the lines and puts out to sea until conditions improve.

Another dramatic example of the port going out to meet the ship has occurred in the recently constructed iron-ore loading facilities at desolate mining camps along South America's west coast. Here, the bulk carrier moors in deep water at the end of a long trestle bridging the distance to shore. A belt carries ore along the trestle from land storage points to the ship. When a section of the ship is filled, the ship is moved forward or aft to a new position, and the ore pours aboard into another hold.

Such installations are keeping port development in line with advances in cargo-handling and with the needs of the peacetime ship. Further change is inevitable. "The ports of the world, which have served mankind so well for numberless centuries," writes Harry C. Brockel of the St. Lawrence Seaway Development Corporation, "have even more important assignments ahead as an essential mechanism in the intricate system of world trade and transport. The ports have traveled in a straight line from the Phoenician galley to the 100,000-ton supership, and we can be reasonably confident that they will continue to be responsive to the ship and the cargo, whatever forms they take."

The Special-purpose Fleet

In the wide world of ships there is a small population of special vessels that, because of their odd looks or unique functions, stand apart from the usual run of freighters, liners and warships. Some of these are glamorous newcomers, like the strange craft at right, which rides on a cushion of air, equally at home over land or water. Akin to it in its high-speed capability is the revolutionary hydrofoil boat, which operates half in, half out of the water. Then there are the working craft, designed to do special jobs: scrappy, high-bowed tugboats, handymen of the harbor; plodding dredges that use buckets, booms and vacuum cleaners to keep the channels clear; slow-moving cable ships that leave trails of telephone lines on the bottom; sturdy, broad-beamed icebreakers that open up the polar seas. Each of these ships, with its strange shape and distinguishing features, is designed to do just one job, and do it better than any other vessel afloat.

AFLOAT ON AIR
Enveloped in spray, the U.S. Navy experimental air-cushion vehicle SKMR-1 rides above the sea on a blast of air created by its four downward-blowing horizontal fans. With a roar, they lift the craft to an altitude of six feet; it is then pushed forward, over land or sea, at speeds greater than 70 knots by its 10-foot stern-mounted propellers. Two airplanelike rudders are behind the propellers.

Its keel five feet above the water, the H. S. (Hydrofoil Ship) *Denison* skims across New York Bay. One of the most advanced hydrofoil boats in

Riding on Underwater Wings

The hulls of the boats shown racing along here are completely out of water. Unlike most high-speed craft, whose hulls plane along the surface, these vessels, called hydrofoils, are riding on underwater foils that support the boat just as wings support an airplane. The foils, attached to the bottom of the boat, are completely submerged when the boat is at rest. But as the craft begins to move, the flow of water past the curved foils creates an upward force similar to the lift provided by airflow around an airplane wing. The faster the boat goes, the more lift is created; as the foils rise in the water they push the hull completely clear of the surface. This means a much faster ride, since the hull's drag is eliminated, and a smoother one, since the hull is unaffected by waves.

The idea of hydrofoils is not new. As early as 1918, Alexander Graham Bell bettered all speedboat records with a pioneer hydrofoil, HD-4, which traveled at 70.85 mph. But practical application of the idea had to wait until 1953, when the first hydrofoil was put in commercial service. As passenger carriers, hydrofoils now ply such waters as the Nile, Italy's Straits of Messina, and the River Plate in South America. The hydrofoil's possible naval role as a submarine chaser is also being investigated. Near-aircraft speeds are promised by jet powered hydrofoils now in the works; one such craft has already "flown" faster than 100 knots.

the U.S., the 118-foot *Denison* can make 60 knots on its three foils—one under the stern, two beneath the stubby extensions amidships.

THE "ARROW" RIDES HIGH

Plying the muddy waters of the River Plate, the *Flecha de Buenos Aires* speeds along at nearly 35 knots on its run between Buenos Aires, Argentina and Colonia, Paraguay. The hydrofoil makes the trip in less than one sixth the time required by the plodding steamers on the same route. The *Flecha* ("Arrow") has two angled foils forward like the one at left, and two at her stern, shrouded by spray in the picture. Because the hull is completely out of the water, the boat's rudder and propeller must be extended down on long shafts so they stay submerged.

Workers of the Waterways

Tugboats are the unglamorous work boats of harbors; in a busy port like New York they constitute nearly one fifth of the ship traffic. Packed into the average tugboat's 100-foot length is more power per ton than is boasted by almost any other kind of ship: more than half its hull space is devoted to engines. The tugboat's pronounced sheer, or curve from bow to stern, is not only pleasing to the eye, but is extremely functional. The familiar high padded bow is needed to push mammoth ocean liners in and out of berths; the long, flat afterdeck leaves plenty of room for handling towlines. The heavy, deep hull lends stability.

Besides herding sleek ocean liners around harbors, tugs tow or push long strings of barges, carrying anything from railroad cars to garbage. Seagoing tugs work on the ocean, helping build offshore oil rigs, rescuing ships in distress and towing hulks across the seas to the scrapyard.

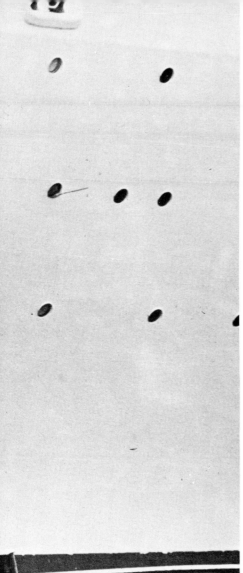

A TOW FOR TWIN FLATTOPS

Stripped and powerless, the veteran World War II aircraft carriers *Guadalcanal* and *Mission Bay* take a last voyage to a Japanese scrapyard, under the charge of the 4,500-horsepower Dutch seagoing tug *Elbe,* one of the largest afloat. The *Elbe's* towing winches automatically compensate for sudden slack or tension in towlines to prevent their parting in heavy seas.

KNEE-HIGH TO AN OCEAN LINER

The 288-gross-ton *Patricia Moran* nudges the liner *Oceanic* into berth. The tug has twin rudders for maneuverability, outsized propellers and a 3,500-horsepower engine. Though her speed is not high (15 knots), *Patricia Moran* can push loads more than 100 times her weight.

TURNING WITHOUT RUDDERS

Fitted with special swiveling propellers which both drive and steer the boat, this rudderless tug can turn a full circle almost within its 98-foot length. The system, called trochoidal drive, is especially suited for vessels operating in the restricted waters of narrow canals or harbors.

The Nautical Mud-scoopers

A dredge is never a handsome craft. Often unpowered and always ungainly, it provides a useful but prosaic service: moving mud. In the busy harbors of the world, dredges of many shapes and sizes keep channels and rivers dug out so other ships can safely pass.

Some dredges are simply barge-mounted steam shovels, well suited for the tight places between piers. Lacking their own motive power, they are moved from job to job by tugs; the muck they haul from the bottom is dumped into waiting barges.

The self-powered dredge works in less confined spaces, like major ship channels, and sucks up mud and water through huge hoses. Some dredges of this type store the slurry, as it is called, in their holds, going out to sea to dump when they are full.

Most efficient for digging out narrow channels is the side-casting boom dredge, shown below neatly clearing a watery path on Lake Maracaibo, Venezuela. Crawling along steadily at about two knots, it cuts a swath in the bottom 115 feet wide, pumping the slurry along its 437-foot boom and squirting it back into the water far outside the limits of the channel.

A SEAGOING VACUUM CLEANER

Crewmen of the dredge *Zulia* ready one of the ship's four drag heads. Two are suspended by cables from the sides of the ship; another pair gets lowered through hatches in the bottom. Dragged along the bottom, they stir up mud, which is sucked through pipes by giant pumps.

HOSING THE WATER WITH MUD

Piped along a swinging boom four fifths the length of the ship itself, a shower of slurry pours from the *Zulia*'s 57-inch-diameter discharge pipe at the rate of 6,000 cubic yards an hour. The boom can also be turned all the way around so that it extends out over the ship's port side.

Stringing Wires on the Bottom

For a century after the first transatlantic telegraph cable was laid in 1858, ships that put down underwater cables were usually vessels converted from other uses. In 1961 the C.S. (Cable Ship) *Long Lines* was launched. Everything about the *Long Lines* is intended to serve her special purpose: five-bladed twin propellers reduce vibration, while a third propeller, set into a tunnel in the bow, enables the ship to make tight turns and hold a steady position; X-ray equipment examines the cable before it goes overboard. Perhaps the most useful of the *Long Lines'* innovations is the linear cable engine, whose job it is to pay out the fragile inch-and-a-quarter cable at a constant speed and tension. Among other things, the cable engine can feed wire adorned with 13-inch amplifiers, prespliced into the cable at 20-mile intervals. It does this without pause; other cable-laying ships have to slow down or stop dead when the amplifiers are encountered.

Storage for cable is provided by three huge cylindrical tanks that take up almost 17 per cent of the ship's hull space. They hold nearly 2,300 miles of cable; under normal conditions the *Long Lines*, steaming at a stately eight knots, can put down the entire load in less than a month.

A CABLE-LAYING MARVEL
The 511-foot *Long Lines* moves out to sea *(above)*, paying out cable through her cloven stern. The linear cable engine, located beneath the helicopter-landing deck near the stern, is supplied with cable from the ship's three storage tanks placed in a bow-to-stern row amidships.

LOOPING MILES OF WIRE
Walking in circles, two men near the one-foot marker as they painstakingly guide cable into one of the *Long Lines'* cable tanks. At the rate of 150 miles a day, loading takes more than two weeks. The tank's central column *(far left)* helps prevent kinking as the cable pays out.

A CABLE GOING ASHORE
With floats attached, one end of a transoceanic cable is towed ashore by a tug *(left)*. The linear cable engine cannot be used in such operations, so the cable must be paid out over bow rollers. The floats will be taken off after the cable has been properly anchored ashore.

DOWN THE CHUTE
On its way to the ocean floor in its last dry moments, cable glides smoothly through the *Long Lines'* stern chute *(right)* at the rate of 800 feet per minute. Though the ship uses mechanical feeders that prevent cable-snapping kinks, the crew must keep a constant watch at the chute.

Opening Up the Polar Seas

Icebreakers are perhaps the most specialized of special ships. They are built with 1⅝-inch steel hulls, specially shaped and heavily reinforced, which allow them to crunch without pause through ice up to three feet thick. Most modern ships are anywhere from seven to nine times longer than they are wide. Icebreakers are much fatter, with a length-to-beam ratio of about 4 to 1—so that the channels they break in the ice will be wider than the ships that follow them. Icebreakers' power requirements are tremendous: their engines turn out as much horsepower as most freighters of twice the length.

When the ice gets really thick—up to 15 feet—an icebreaker can resort to the "whack and back" method. Backing off several hundred feet, it heads full speed for the ice. Sloping bows and rounded hulls allow the craft to slide up onto the ice, which cracks under the weight—and then the ship backs up for another whack.

CLEARING THE WAY FOR FOOD
In the vanguard of a supply mission, the U.S. Navy icebreaker *Edisto (top)* and the Coast Guard's *Northwind* cut a swath of open water through the thick Antarctic ice. Although mainly concerned with opening channels for other ships, icebreakers are called upon to rescue icebound ships, and often represent the only reliable line of supply for polar research bases.

MOVING A MOUNTAIN OF ICE
Clearing McMurdo Sound Channel, a principal supply route for Antarctic bases, the Navy icebreaker *Atka* pushes a vast one-and-a-half-million-ton iceberg out to sea. Breakers are often at sea for months at a time and must therefore carry an abnormally large fuel supply. For their large crews—the average is 230—the larders stock enough provisions to last nearly a year.

BLASTING A POLAR PATHWAY
Under the midnight sun, the *Burton Island*, assisted by well-placed charges of TNT, pushes through to a scientific station at Cape Hallett in Antarctica. Even with the aid of explosives, a breaker's progress is often so slowed by thick ice that it makes less than a mile in 24 hours.

6

Revolution beneath the Sea

A POLARIS SUBMARINE, ONE OF THE MOST POTENT WARSHIPS EVER BUILT, IS LAUNCHED AT NEWPORT NEWS, VIRGINIA.

ON JANUARY 17, 1955, U.S.S. *Nautilus*, the U.S. Navy's Submarine No. 571, long, low, dark and deadly looking in the wintry chop, moved into the main channel of Connecticut's Thames River on her first sea trial. Her signal light blinked a historic message to the shore: "Under way on nuclear power." Those five words marked the end of one era of the fighting ship and the birth of another.

Aircraft carriers had ended the age of the battleship in World War II. Now the roles of the destroyers and other surface fighting craft, with the possible exception of the carrier, would soon be sharply reduced to police duty and use in "limited" wars. The forerunner of what would be a decisive element in the nuclear standoff of major powers slipped out of sight, out of radar reach, beneath the surface of the sea.

Nautilus was the world's first nuclear-powered ship, and the world's first true submarine. Unlike her predecessors, which were essentially specialized surface vessels which could submerge for short periods, her natural home was under the sea. Powered by several pounds of uranium fuel, she could travel great distances and remain submerged for incredible lengths of time.

On her shakedown cruise in May 1955, the *Nautilus* ran underwater all the way from New London to San Juan, Puerto Rico—1,602 statute miles in 84 hours—shattering all previous submarine records for speed, endurance and range. In 1957, she became the first ship to cruise beneath the Arctic ice cap. The next year, she carried 116 men on a 2,000-mile voyage under the North Pole, across the top of the world from Bering Strait to the Greenland Sea.

In the years since the *Nautilus* first set out from New London, the nuclear submarine has become even larger, faster and more self-sufficient. Capable of spending 99.5 per cent of its time at sea underwater, of remaining submerged for months on end, of traveling more than 100,000 miles—several times around the earth—without refueling, the modern submarine is all but independent of land bases and the surface of the water.

By 1965 there were more than 50 of the new breed in the U.S. Navy, more than half of them carrying Polaris missiles. Together, the 16 missiles aboard each Polaris-armed submarine have more explosive power than all the bombs dropped by both sides in World War II. The Polaris solid-fuel rocket, tipped with a hydrogen warhead, has a range of 2,800 miles. For the first time in history, a sea-based weapons system can obliterate any land target in the world.

The submarine's 100-odd men and officers—all highly trained specialists in nucleonics, electronics and other nuclear-age sciences—live in a strange, detached, hermetically sealed world. The sea itself provides two of the requisites for life. Generators decompose water by electrolysis into its components and thus manufacture an endless supply of oxygen. Distillers turn salt water into fresh. There are certain amenities as well. The ship carries enough air-conditioning equipment to cool a fair-sized town on a July afternoon. There are ice cream machines, au-

123

NEGATIVE BUOYANCY

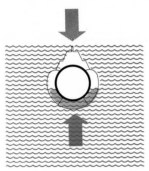

NEUTRAL BUOYANCY

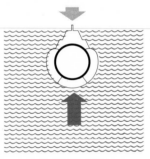

POSITIVE BUOYANCY

A SUB'S UPS AND DOWNS result from variations in two opposing forces: buoyancy *(green arrows)*, exerted by the water, and gravity *(gray arrows)*, determined by the ship's weight. When a submarine's tanks are filled with water, it has more weight than buoyancy and it descends *(top)*. With part of the water blown out of its tanks, the sub reaches neutral buoyancy: the forces are equal and the vessel hovers. With the tanks fully discharged, buoyancy gains the advantage over gravity, and the sub rises to the surface.

tomatic washers and dryers, fresh-water showers, movies, several small libraries, hi-fi sound systems and a host of other conveniences and luxuries plus the best chow in the U.S. Navy.

In the control center is the inertial navigation system whose spinning gyros, transistorized computers and circuitry make the submarine independent of celestial and radio-beacon navigation. Highly sensitive accelerometers—delicate contrivances of weights and springs—sense and register every change in the ship's speed, depth, direction or position, and feed the information to computers operating on "real time." A "real-time" computer can absorb and use data so quickly that it can analyze a happening while it is taking place. Such a machine is employed to regulate space flights because its description of the current state of the capsule is only milliseconds behind the actual state. Similarly, the computer aboard a submarine can give the ship's precise location in an instant. Actually there are three inertial navigation systems aboard which keep a constant check on the accuracy of one another.

There are at least five other computer systems in the modern submarine. One programs sextant sightings and radio-navigational signals taken when the vessel is near enough to the surface for the periscope and radio equipment to be used. Another computes trajectories for missile guidance, using information from the inertial navigation system, while a third controls the launching of the rockets, which can be fired at about one-minute intervals. The fourth system integrates readings from the complex array of sonar listening gear that locates enemy surface ships and submarines, and then sets up aiming and firing directions. The fifth utilizes the information to determine the exact moment for the firing of torpedoes.

The bottle principle

Despite all the new gear, a nuclear submarine has the same fundamental operating principle as its predecessors: controlled buoyancy. An empty bottle, tossed on rough water, will float for a while. Filled with air, the bottle has positive buoyancy. When water washes in, displacing part of the air, the bottle becomes heavier and heavier until it is just on the verge of sinking; it has neutral buoyancy. The moment it takes in additional water and weighs more than the displaced water, the bottle sinks because it has negative buoyancy. If there were a way of gradually blowing out the water and replacing it with air, neutral and then positive buoyancy would be restored, and the bottle would return to the surface.

Through controlled application of this physical principle, a submarine rides on the surface, submerges, remains under at the desired depth and rises to the surface again. The ship has an inner pressure hull and a lighter outer hull, and the space between them is compartmented into a series of tanks. The submarine's degree of buoyancy is regulated by allowing sea water to flow into the tanks, and by emptying them with pumps or "blowing" them with compressed air.

When the sub is about to get underway, the diving chief floods all tanks except the main ballast and bow buoyancy tanks. One of those filled at this time is the negative tank, which is located forward of the center of the ship and will give it a downward angle when it submerges. At this stage, the ship still has positive buoyancy. To dive, the remaining tanks are filled and the submarine achieves negative buoyancy. When the gauges show she has just about reached the desired depth, enough water is blown from the negative tank to establish neutral buoyancy. Trim tanks are used to maintain the neutral buoyancy and to keep the ship on an even keel. To surface, water is forced from the bow tank to make the forward end lighter than the rest of the ship, thus pointing her at an angle toward the surface. Then the main ballast tanks are gradually emptied until the submarine regains positive buoyancy and is again floating on the top.

How to maneuver underwater

The submarine is not, of course, maneuvered by tanks alone. Her propeller drives her in the direction in which she is pointed—downward, upward or horizontally. Like a surface ship, she has rudders which steer her to left or right. In addition, the modern submarine has two pairs of diving planes, small movable wings which function like the elevator on an airplane. One pair is mounted forward, extending from either side of the vessel's dorsal superstructure, or "sail," which houses the periscope, radio antenna and the surface navigating bridge. The other pair projects from either side of the stern.

When the submarine is diving, the leading edges of the forward planes are tilted downward, and the water flowing by exerts a downward pressure on the surfaces. The stern planes are tilted in the opposite direction, and the force of the water lifts the stern of the ship. To ascend, the respective positions of the forward and stern planes are reversed. Thus, when a submarine dives or climbs, three elements play a part in the maneuver: tanks, propeller and planes.

On older submarines, one member of the crew operates the rudder, a second the forward diving planes, and a third the stern planes. In the latest subs, one man, called the planesman, can control all of these functions. Strapped to his seat like an aircraft pilot, he guides the ship with a yoke—a steering wheel mounted on a shaft that moves forward and backward, something like the control column in an airplane. To go to the left or right, the planesman turns the wheel. To dive, he pushes the shaft forward; to climb, he pulls it toward him. And, as on a plane, the planesman has a "co-pilot" with duplicate controls.

Maximum depth and maximum underwater speed for nuclear submarines are, of course, secret information. However, knowledgeable observers estimate that the new ships can travel at over 30 knots and descend 1,200 to 1,500 feet beneath the surface.

Like the airplane, the submarine reached its present stage of development through the dreams and efforts of inspired, brave and, sometimes, even crackpot men. Man's desire to explore the underwater world is probably as old as his wish to fly. To realize this ambition, early visionaries dived beneath the surfaces of rivers, lakes and harbors in a wild variety of man-powered and often suicidal contraptions.

In the early 1600s, Cornelis Drebbel submerged in a boat made of wood covered with greased leather, and propelled by oars. During the American Revolution David Bushnell's one-man *Turtle*, equipped with a breathing tube that was a forerunner of the German snorkel of World War II, and driven by crank and propeller, became the first submarine to engage in naval warfare. Sergeant Ezra Lee of the Continental Army took the craft under the British warship H.M.S. *Eagle*, anchored in New York Harbor, and attempted to attach a delayed-action mine to her hull. However, Lee couldn't get the screw fastener into the copper-sheathed planking, and the mine floated away and blew up harmlessly in the water.

Although undersea craft were still powered by men—either by arm cranks or treadmills—during the early decades of the 19th Century, the vessels were becoming more sophisticated. In 1801, Robert Fulton, who was later to design the first successful steamboat, built for Napoleon Bonaparte a submarine called the *Nautilus*, which had the first diving plane. Despite her successful tests, Napoleon lost interest.

The undersea coffin

One of the last of the man-powered submarines was built during the Civil War. The Confederate *H. L. Hunley*, sometimes known as "the Peripatetic Coffin," was the key element in a daring scheme to break the Union blockade of Charleston Harbor. The vessel was financed by Captain Horace L. Hunley of the Confederate Army and built by two Confederate marine engineers, J. R. McClintock and Baxter Watson. She was a modified iron boiler, enlarged to 30 feet in length, and achieved depth control by means of ballast tanks, detachable weights and a pair of five-foot diving planes. She had a depth gauge and was illuminated by a candle which also served as an oxygen-level indicator. Unless she was close enough to the surface for her skipper to see out of glass plates in her hatchway coamings, he had to steer blindly. Eight men working a crankshaft connected to a three-bladed stern propeller gave her a calm-water speed of four miles an hour. Initially, her armament consisted of a floating copper mine, packed with 90 pounds of gunpowder and towed at the end of a 200-foot line. Her attack plan was to dive beneath an anchored enemy ship, surface on the far side and keep going until she pulled the mine against the target and destroyed it.

Though ultimately she won a niche in history as the first submarine to sink an enemy vessel, the *Hunley*'s war record was a grim pageant of disaster. While she was lying at her Charleston wharf, preparing to leave for a trial dive with all crewmen at their stations, the swell from a passing steamer rolled over her deck and poured into her open hatches. She filled and sank instantly, taking with her all hands except her commanding officer, Lieutenant John Payne, who escaped through an open hatch. Payne supervised her salvage and recruited a new crew of volunteers. In early fall of 1863, she swamped and sank again, this time while tied up at Fort Sumter. Only Payne and two crewmen escaped. Again she was raised.

Panic in the dark

Now Captain Hunley himself took command. On October 15, in full view of a large crowd of spectators, Hunley submerged in a test dive in Charleston Harbor. He flooded the forward tanks too heavily and too soon. She tilted and plunged under. Her candle was unlit. The crew panicked in the blackness. She drove her bow into the harbor mud and stayed there, with the loss of all hands.

For a third time, the *Hunley* was raised and refitted. Now she was armed with a spar torpedo—a torpedo fastened to a long pole projecting from her stem. On the night of February 17, 1864, under command of Lieutenant George E. Dixon, she moved stealthily out of Charleston Harbor. Her intended victim was the Union warship U.S.S. *Housatonic*, a few miles off the harbor entrance. At first, the watch on the *Housatonic* thought the *Hunley* was a floating plank. The submarine bore in and struck the warship on the starboard quarter. The explosion tore the *Housatonic* apart. The warship sank instantly, taking the *Hunley* and all hands down with her. All but five of the *Housatonic*'s crew survived the attack.

By the 1880s, many surface ships were being built with mechanical propulsion, and it was tried with submarines, too. Steam proved impractical. A furnace created great heat and consumed oxygen, and therefore could not be used when the craft was submerged. Experimenters tried building up a head of reserve steam, then dousing the fires and waiting for the boat to cool off before submerging, but they had little success.

For a while, the new miracle of electricity, supplied by storage batteries, seemed to provide the solution, and in 1886, Andrew Campbell and James Ash, both Englishmen, designed a submarine (also called the *Nautilus*) powered by two 45-horsepower electric motors. The vessel had a speed of six to eight knots and a range of 80 miles.

Naval authorities soon took an interest in electric-powered submarines. The French and Italian Navies launched battery-driven submarines displacing as much as 95 tons on the surface. Spain built one that logged 10 knots on the surface and eight submerged; in 1890, it performed

AN ILL-FATED SUB, the tiny Confederate vessel *Hunley* was the first undersea craft ever to sink an enemy warship. Built from a 25-foot-long iron boiler, the *Hunley* was little more than a seagoing coffin: in trials she sank at least three times with her crew. Finally, on the night of February 17, 1864, she rammed a torpedo into the Union ship *Housatonic* anchored in the blockaded harbor of Charleston. A Southern newspaper *(above)* hailed the triumph; but the *Hunley* went down with her target.

brilliantly with new, self-propelled torpedoes fitted with dummy heads, scoring three hits out of three tries on a target ship. Strangely enough, Spanish officials were not impressed. They concluded that ". . . the ship as constructed served no useful purpose," and shelved the project as a failure. About a decade later, U.S. Admiral George Dewey voiced a far different opinion about the submarine as a fighting ship. "If they had had two of those things at Manila," he said, referring to his Philippine Island victory over the Spanish fleet in 1898, "I could never have held it with the squadron I had."

But the electric submarine had one glaring limitation: there was no way of recharging batteries at sea. The craft could cruise for about 80 miles. Then the captain had to order an immediate return to port or risk having the entire power plant go dead.

Help from the horseless carriage

In the late 1890s, two American inventors and submarine designers, John P. Holland and Simon Lake, independently but almost simultaneously arrived at the solution: the gasoline engine that was already powering many of the new horseless carriages. Because of its need of oxygen for combustion, the automobile engine could not be used when the submarine was submerged. However, when the craft was on the surface and the hatches open, the engine could operate a generator to recharge batteries, and it could also propel the ship.

The U.S. Navy accepted Holland's first submarine of the new type in 1900. The *Holland* was nearly 54 feet long, displaced about 75 tons when submerged and had a range of 1,500 miles. It performed extremely well. Holland designed five subs similar to the *Holland* for Japan and built seven of a larger type for the United States.

Lake launched his gasoline-engine-and-battery submarine, the *Protector*, in 1902. He sold it and several others like it to Russia. Later, he also built submarines for Austria and, finally, for the United States. However, Lake's greatest contribution to the submarine was sight. Until he solved the problem, all submarines, including his own, traveled blind when submerged. To learn what lay ahead, the skipper had to bring the craft almost to the surface so that he could see through the porthole of the conning tower. Cruising "on the surface with the conning tower exposed . . . would only be a target in wartime," Lake said. He set out to remedy the situation by creating a "seeing eye . . . so small it will not attract attention." A simple periscope such as a child might make would not be good enough since it sharply reduced both the area of vision and the size of the image. The instrument Lake wanted to construct would have to magnify the image and provide a wide angle of vision.

Knowing little of optics, Lake bought a haphazard collection of prisms, mirrors and lenses, and began trying them out in various combinations. It was slow, tedious work shifting the parts about on a board he used as a base. He had no guiding theory; his experiments were purely empirical. He would simply arrange the pieces of glass, stick the board out of his office window and hope to see at right angles to the way he was facing. Finally, one day in 1902, he hit upon the correct combination. The street and harbor he had hoped to see were now clearly visible. At this moment, he was called to an inner office. He left the equipment where it was. When he returned a few moments later, he found to his dismay that at the height of a sudden shower, an office boy had pulled the board out of the rain and dismantled the arrangement. After days of futile attempts to reestablish it, Lake went to a professor of optics at Johns Hopkins for assistance. Together, they finally managed to reassemble the parts correctly. Lake now went on to perfect his "omniscope," the forerunner of both the fixed and rotating periscope. The submarine now had its "seeing eye."

Although the submarine could now see when submerged and could travel considerable distances, there remained one dangerous problem. Gasoline fumes could never be completely eliminated from the interior of the ship. At almost any time, these volatile fumes could flash into a hull-rending explosion.

The solution, which established the form of the submarine's propulsion system until nuclear power came along, was provided by the diesel engine, invented by the German engineer Rudolf Diesel in the 1890s. Fired by compression rather than by electric spark, the diesel burned cheaper fuel oil and ran more economically than the gasoline engine. Far more important, the fumes were less toxic and volatile. Britain pioneered with the new engine in 1908. Four years later, the U.S. launched its first submarine that used diesel engines on the surface and batteries while submerged. Germany soon followed with its long, heavy, diesel-powered Unterseeboote, or U-boats, as they were known through two world wars.

The unseen terror

It was the German Navy in World War I which first showed what a terrifyingly effective fighting ship the submarine could be. In September 1914, the U-9 sank three British cruisers in slightly more than 90 minutes in the North Sea. In the four years that followed, German submarines sent more than 11 million tons of Allied shipping to the bottom. Both sides used the craft with enormous effect in the Second World War. In the Atlantic, Germany destroyed over 14 million tons of Allied merchant shipping. In the Pacific, U.S. submarines sank nearly 1,400 Japanese ships, displacing some 5,600,000 tons.

During the several decades that followed the introduction of the diesel engine, designers increased the submarine's range, speed and the depth at which it could safely operate. Attack-warning and detection systems were added and then improved upon. But the submarine still retained one often fatal weakness: the need to come up to recharge batteries. Even the largest batteries could drive the ship for only 40 to 48 hours, at a top speed of two and a half knots. Then, no matter where she was, the submarine had to come to the surface, turn on the diesel engines and wait until the generators had restored power for underwater operations.

During World War II, Germany was especially hard hit by this inherent flaw in the submarine. By mid-1942, Allied patrol bombers had radar detection gear. Fog or darkness no longer protected U-boats when they surfaced to recharge batteries. Often they would find themselves under attack before they could dive to safety. The need to diminish this vulnerability led to two important advances by German scientists.

The first was the *schnorchel*—German slang for "snout," and modified in American usage to "snorkel"—a modernization of surface ventilation tubes used at least as far back as Bushnell and his *Turtle*. The snorkel, still standard equipment on most conventionally powered submarines, is essentially a pair of fixed air pipes projecting from the submarine's topside, one to bring in fresh air for engines and crew, the other to exhaust engine fumes. Valves prevent the entry of sea water. The device enables a submarine to breathe underwater, to run on diesels or to charge her batteries with a fair degree of concealment.

Nevertheless, the pipes were far from perfect. For one thing they required sturdy housing—a breathing mast which left a wake visible from the air. Also, the submarine still had to remain within a few feet of the surface to use its snorkel, and it was incapable of a quick dive if caught off guard. Moreover, despite a soft-rubber shielding the Germans applied to the housing, it reflected the very high frequency radar pulses of Allied surface ships and so betrayed the U-boat's presence. However, hunter-killer planes now had far more difficulty locating the submarine with their radar equipment.

A dramatic approach

The second countermeasure was more than a limited mechanical device; it was rather a profound innovation in power plants—a dramatic reach for the key to the true submarine: the engine that could operate in total independence from atmospheric air. It was known as the Walther closed-cycle, hydrogen peroxide engine.

As early as 1933, Hellmuth Walther, a German scientist, had been fascinated with the potential of hydrogen peroxide—the same liquid used in bleaching—as a fuel in new propulsion systems. He had designed and tested both rocket and aircraft motors, and in 1937 offered the German Navy plans for a submarine commander's dream: a self-sufficient, self-contained, high-speed turbine engine. Walther's ingenious engine used chemical catalysts to break down hydrogen peroxide into water and oxygen. The liberated oxygen was fed into a combustion chamber with diesel fuel. The diesel oil burned in the oxygen at a high temperature. Water injected into the combustion chamber cooled the gas from the burning oil and became high-pressure steam. The steam and the burned-oil gas were fed into a conventional turbine, which supplied power for propulsion. Thus, the submarine carried oxygen for power combustion whenever it went under the surface—in its own fuel supply.

Belatedly, in May 1944, Hitler authorized construction of 100 Type XXVI U-boats, to be powered by Walther engines. They were to be relatively small—850 tons surface displacement—submarines with a top submerged speed of no less than 25 knots. Nothing the Allies had in antisubmarine devices could have stopped them. However, Allied bombing of German shipyards made the problem academic; production of the vessels was delayed, and the war ended before a Type XXVI boat could be completed and launched. In the 1950s, the British Navy built two experimental submarines, *Explorer* and *Excalibur*, and powered them with Walther-cycle engines. They performed exceptionally well, but with the laying of the keel of U.S.S. *Nautilus*, on June 14, 1952, they ceased to have a future. Atomic power had rendered them obsolete.

The nuclear revolution

The first proposal of a nuclear submarine for the U.S. Navy was made by Dr. Ross Gunn of the Naval Research Laboratory in the late 1930s, long before the Manhattan Project began to develop the atomic bomb. In 1946, Dr. Philip H. Abelson, also of the Laboratory, presented plans for the power plant of such a ship. The actual work began soon afterward under the remarkable leadership of Captain (later Vice Admiral) Hyman G. Rickover.

The heart of the nuclear submarine was to be controlled nuclear fission, and for this, of course, a nuclear reactor or furnace was necessary. To design and make one that would work within the severe space limitations of a submarine, and then to redesign the submarine itself to carry such a furnace, required one of the most creative and far-ranging research and development programs in the history of engineering. It became necessary to push back the frontiers of a dozen different scientific fields: physics, metallurgy, electronics, fluid dynamics, ceramics, environmental medicine, plastics. Rare materials such as hafnium for the reactor safety rods and zirconium for sheathing the uranium fuel had to be produced in quantity for the first time. Totally new mechanical devices—leakproof, water-lubricated pumps, for example—had to be invented, tested, perfected and manufactured in volume.

The resulting vessel was once characterized by Dr. George Kistiakowsky, President Eisenhower's science adviser, as "a breathtaking microcosm of American technology." Heat produced by controlled fission in the reactor is transferred to water in sealed pipes; the water reaches a high temperature because it is under such great pressure that it is

A NUCLEAR POWER PLANT in a submarine does its work in two cycles. In the primary cycle *(gray)*, atomic fission in the sub's reactor heats water to temperatures far above the normal boiling point—but under pressure, so it does not turn to steam. When the heat is transferred to the water in the secondary cycle *(green)*, this water does turn to steam. The steam flows through a turbine to drive the vessel's propeller, and then condenses and returns to the steam generator for reheating.

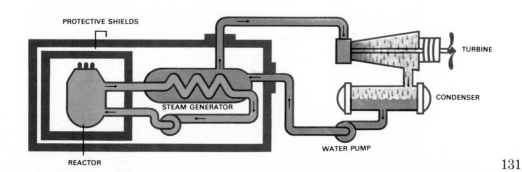

prevented from boiling. Pumps drive the superheated water to the steam generator where the heat is transmitted to a second water system; in this system the water is under low pressure and therefore boils. The steam created by the boiling water is fed to the engine room to spin the turbines. They, in turn, drive the propeller and operate the generators that provide the ship's electricity. Once the steam passes through the turbines, it is condensed back into water and returned to the steam generator.

Controls that would automatically shut down the reactor in an emergency render an atomic accident functionally impossible. Shielding around the power plants keep the radiation level when submerged lower than it is from natural sources in the average American backyard or city street. The amount of fuel used by the nuclear power plant is minute. In the *Nautilus'* first 10 years in service, she traveled about 330,000 miles, of which more than 255,000, or about 77 per cent, were submerged. In that period, *Nautilus* used only three reactor cores—perhaps a dozen pounds of uranium fuel. Had she burned diesel oil, she would have consumed almost 10 million gallons—enough to fill a railroad tank-car train nine miles long.

The ship and the weapon

After the launching of the *Nautilus*, two more revolutionary achievements of technology remained before the submarine became the ship that would rewrite the books of naval and military strategy. In the nuclear reactor-steam turbine engine, the submersible vessel had achieved the requisite power plant for a true submarine. Now, she needed the ultimate hydrodynamic shape and the ultimate weapon. Within five years of the commissioning of *Nautilus*, the submarine had them both: the form was that of *Albacore;* the weapon was the Polaris.

In 1949, the Navy's Bureau of Ships acknowledged that undersea control of the traditional submarine design became both difficult and hazardous at speeds of over 20 knots, and the resistance to water was far too high. Taylor Model Basin was authorized to develop a new high-speed hull form. After exhaustive experiments with more than 30 different models, Taylor researchers settled on the one that still distinguishes the newer American nuclear submarine: a rounded bow, tapering to the tail, giving the vessel the shape of the blimp and the whale; length-to-beam ratio 7.6 to 1 (as contrasted to the World War II fleet submarine's needlelike 11.5 to 1), a single propeller—instead of the two the *Nautilus* has—and vertical rudders and horizontal diving planes just forward of the propeller.

In 1953, these features of the successful model were incorporated in the 210-foot *Albacore*, the only naval ship ever built solely for hydrodynamic research. Stripped of torpedo tubes and other military equipment, she was crammed with diesel engines and batteries to give her underwater speeds, still classified, that may have reached 35 to 40 knots. In her trials she scored a spectacular success. Easily, almost lazily,

E-CLASS. 1911

GATO CLASS. 1941

"GUPPY" TYPE. 1949

ALBACORE. 1953

NAUTILUS. 1954

SKIPJACK. 1958

LAFAYETTE CLASS. 1963

EVOLUTION OF SUBMARINE DESIGN in the U.S. Navy is depicted above. Because of their air-breathing diesel engines, early subs often ran on the surface and their hull lines resembled those of surface ships. This feature was retained in the first nuclear sub, *Nautilus*. But a year earlier the diesel-driven *Albacore* was designed with an experimental whalelike hull that greatly reduced underwater resistance. Nuclear drive and whale shape were first combined in the *Skipjack*, precursor of the modern, missile-carrying *Lafayette* class.

she traveled at the speed of the fastest fleet submarine in the Navy on one fourth the power. Her advances in controllability were so remarkable that her officers coined the word "hydrobatics" to describe her stuntlike maneuvers. She not only banked and turned like a plane but could even make the tight climbing curve that fliers call a chandelle.

Albacore hull and nuclear power were combined for the first time in 252-foot *Skipjack*, launched in May 1958. She had *Albacore*'s single propeller and introduced the now-characteristic sail planes. She ran faster than any other submarine in history.

The sub killers

Skipjack is not equipped to carry Polaris missiles. She and her five sister ships are a new kind of submarine, one whose primary mission is to hunt down and kill enemy submarines. Her sonar detection equipment is highly sensitive and she is armed with six torpedo tubes in her bow. Later models of such submarines are equipped with SUBROC (for SUBmarine ROCket), an underwater missile that gets to an enemy submarine by traveling primarily through the air. The rocket is blasted to the surface and flies through the sky until it is near the target. Then the rocket releases a torpedo or nuclear depth charge by parachute. After falling into the water, the depth charge explodes; the torpedo homes in on the victim like a conventional torpedo.

Polaris, the end product of a five-year, $3.5-billion research and development program, first emerged in 1955 from a joint Army-Navy experimental project seeking to develop nuclear-armed ballistic missiles. An epic effort by Navy's Special Projects Office and its Chief, Rear Admiral (later Vice Admiral) William F. Raborn Jr., succeeded five years later in producing Polaris A-1, a guided missile to be launched from a submerged submarine. It was the world's first long-range, solid-fuel missile—28 feet in length, 4½ feet in diameter, weighing about 15 tons and shaped like a champagne bottle. It was to carry a nuclear warhead 1,400 miles. A shot of compressed air would boost it from its launching tube. When it broke free of the surface, its two-stage rocket motor would ignite, lift it into a predetermined trajectory, send it screaming through the stratosphere at an estimated speed of 12,000 miles per hour, then drop off and leave the missile to hurtle on to its target. Initial testing from land pads began at Cape Canaveral, now Cape Kennedy, late in September 1958. The first five missiles tested were failures. But the sixth, in April 1959, roared off the launcher, flamed into the sky and went flying [triumphantly] down the range to its target.

Even as Admiral Raborn and his crew were testing Polaris, the first submarine designed to carry the missile, U.S.S. *George Washington*, was taking shape on the ways at New London. She slid into the Thames River in Connecticut on June 9, 1959. Three hundred and eighty-one feet long, displacing 5,900 tons on the surface, she had, when armed, the mightiest and most destructive weapons system that the world had ever seen. A little more than a year later—July 20, 1960, at 39 minutes past noon—she successfully launched a Polaris missile from underwater 25 miles east of Cape Canaveral. She fired another at 3:32 p.m. Admiral Raborn and Commander James B. Osborn, skipper of the *George Washington,* flashed the historic news to President Eisenhower: "Polaris— from out of the deep to target. Perfect."

By 1965 there were 29 Polaris-armed submarines in the U.S. Navy, each patrolling her station beneath the seas of the world. No surprise attack could knock them out. A missile launching site on land can be easily located, but no enemy could possibly know where these hidden, constantly moving ships would be at any given moment. Widely scattered around the globe, they had every possible land target within their combined range. The accurate, nuclear-tipped missiles they fire could devastate huge areas.

The Soviet Union, of course, has similar submarines and nuclear missile systems. Other nations are developing them. Whether man will avoid or cause the holocaust he is now capable of producing depends to a great degree upon these instruments of destruction. Will their awesome potential prevent a major war, or encourage reckless aggression?

The position of the United States was summed up by Admiral Raborn. "Get a deterrent they can't get at," he said. "That will keep us all here together."

Changing Shapes of Ships at War

Through history nations have fought for control of the sea with ever more powerful warships, at ever greater distances. For 3,000 years sea battles in the Mediterranean were decided by huge rowboats carrying waterborne armies of trained marines; ramming, boarding and man-to-man fighting were the tactics of the day. In the 16th Century cannon and sail began to open the range between vessels, and for 300 years stately, wind-powered ships of the line slugged it out broadside to broadside. With the Industrial Revolution came major changes: steam, the propeller, iron armor, explosive shells, revolving turret guns. The wooden man-of-war evolved into the steel dreadnought. Then the rule of the mighty battleship was challenged by two new weapons, the torpedo and the aerial bomb: by the last great naval battles of World War II, the submarine and the aircraft carrier had achieved a dominance they have not yet relinquished.

A MIGHTY BROADSIDE

Framed by a jungle of rigging and a massive five-ton anchor, open gunports reveal some of the stout armament of H.M.S. *Victory,* Lord Nelson's flagship at the battle of Trafalgar. Most famous of the great wooden ships of the line, *Victory* carried 104 cannon on five decks, including some that fired ponderous, 32-pound balls. She is now preserved in dry dock at Portsmouth, England.

First Battleship: The Trireme

The early civilizations of the Mediterranean settled their disputes at sea by means of long, fast, graceful wooden ships called galleys. These ships were moved by scores of rowers, and carried marines and a ship-sinking weapon: the ram. In those often windless waters only oars could be relied on for maneuvering in battle, and the galleys carried their square sails mainly for cruising—or fleeing.

The first galleys had single banks of oars, but to increase their speed and maneuverability, the developing navies of Egypt, Phoenicia and Greece progressed to two-banked galleys and

finally to the three-banked trireme *(shown here)*. Each oar was pulled by one man, while a flute player or drummer sounded the stroke. (Contrary to general belief, the rowers in most ancient navies were not slaves and the lash was unknown.) In sprints the oarsmen could move their ship as fast as 10 knots; with one side backing water they could spin it in a tight circle. But with a freeboard of eight feet and a draft of only three, the trireme was not seaworthy. It also lacked space for sleeping and provisions; at night or in bad weather it was customarily hauled ashore.

But a trireme, properly employed, could be an awesome tool of war. At the Battle of Salamis (in 480 B.C.), where both sides used triremes, a small Greek force routed a Persian fleet of some 800 ships as they entered the narrow confines of a bay near Athens. The Greeks counterattacked just as a wind sprang up behind the Persians, piling their rear ranks into the retreating advance guard. Mercilessly, the Greeks sank boat after boat with their underwater rams, lunging and backing off so deftly the Persians could make little use of their overwhelming numbers.

THE SITE OF A TRAP

Scene of the classic battle between Greek and Persian galleys was this strait between the port of Piraeus and the island of Salamis *(background)*. As the Persian ruler Xerxes watched, probably not far from where this photograph was taken, his scores of triremes advanced around the point at left. The Greeks, drawn up in the narrows at right, feigned retreat to bring the Persians crowding in, then suddenly attacked and demolished their narrowed front.

A GREEK MAN-OF-WAR

The largest Greek trireme, like the one above, was 125 feet long, 20 feet wide, and carried 170 oarsmen, 30 sailors, 14 spear bearers and four archers. Its major weapon was the ram, a menacing, metal-tipped extension of the keel.

FEMININE WILES AT SALAMIS

In this 19th Century painting of the Battle of Salamis a Persian admiral-queen named Artemisia is seen escaping disaster by ramming another Persian galley. Thinking her an ally, the Greeks veered off and she fled with her ships.

Gunpowder Dooms the Galley

Two thousand years after Salamis, Mediterranean sea battles were still being fought by galleys. Because good rowers were hard to find, brawn had been substituted for skill: ships now had single banks of oars with as many as five men to an oar. Moreover, the ancient technique of ramming had largely given way to grappling and boarding, with the attacking swordsmen often using their ship's above-water beak as a gangplank.

But gunpowder had already numbered the galley's days. At the Battle of Lepanto in 1571—the last great clash between galley fleets, which pitted Christians against Turks—vessels of both sides carried a few cannon in their bows. But what assured victory for the Christians were six Venetian galleasses—ponderous men-of-war, half-galley, half-sailing ship, which mounted 30 guns each. To close with the main line of Christian ships, the Turks had to sail directly past these floating fortresses. Their thunderous broadsides threw the Turks' classic galley formation into fatal confusion, and presaged the advent of the warship as a floating gun platform.

AT THE HEIGHT OF BATTLE
A violent melee during the Battle of Lepanto off the west coast of Greece is shown in this old Venetian painting, with the Turkish vessels flying crescent flags and the Christians flying crosses. Three galleasses, their broadside guns clearly visible, are seen at upper right.

THE LINEUP AT LEPANTO
In this 16th Century fresco the two opposing forces at Lepanto are shown before the conflict, drawn up in squadrons abreast in an order of battle borrowed from land warfare. Leading the Christian fleet *(left)* are the six three-masted galleasses that decided the course of battle.

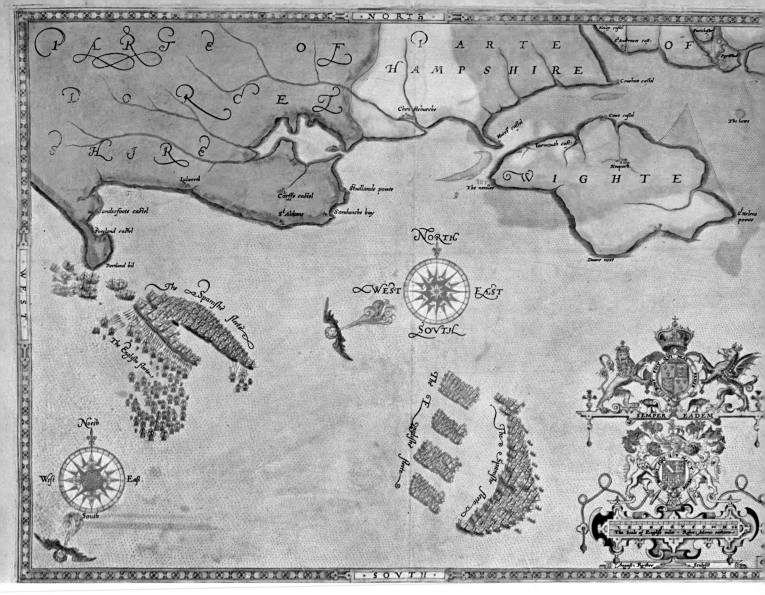

ATTACKING THE CRESCENT

Engraved charts of the period *(above and at right)* illustrate the week's fighting in the Channel that ended in the Armada's rout. At far left the English fleet has circled out with its faster ships to gain the windward advantage and is engaging in a furious battle with the tightly disciplined Spanish fleet. The next day the English form four squadrons *(center)* to harass the defensive Spanish crescent and catch stragglers.

Faster Sail and Longer Guns

In the 16th Century, while oar-powered galleys still dominated the Mediterranean, the oceangoing nations of the Atlantic coast had turned the sailing ship into a long-range instrument of exploration, piracy and trade. But its full-fledged debut as a man-of-war did not come until Philip II of Spain sent his "invincible" Armada to invade England in 1588. The failure of Philip's 124-ship fleet has been attributed to many causes, from an inexperienced admiral to leaky water casks. But there seems little question that the deciding factors were superior English ships and guns.

For a decade Elizabeth's zealous sea commander and naval architect, John Hawkins, who did not believe in man-to-man fighting at sea, had been remodeling Her Majesty's vessels into swift craft decked to carry long-range culverins, cast-brass cannon which could throw a relatively light (nine- or 17-pound) round shot with some accuracy more than a mile.

With nimbler ships that could sail closer to the wind, the British squadrons under Sir Francis Drake and other commanders stayed to windward of the Spaniards up the Channel, controlling the fighting distance, never letting the enemy grapple and board with their heavy infantry. By frustrating the Armada, those inventive sailors saved England. They also showed that henceforward sea battles would be won not by waterborne soldiers, but by sailors, guns and ships.

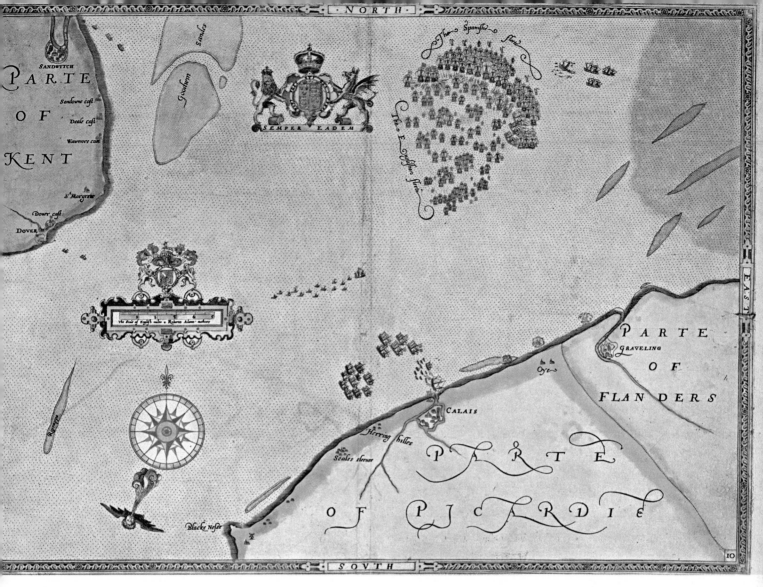

SANDWITCH
PARTE
OF
KENT
Sandowne cast
Deale cast
Watemore cast
St Margarete
Dover cast
DOVER

Goodwyn Stands

The Scale of English miles • Roberto Adams Authorr

SEMPER EADEM

The Spanyshe flete
The English flete

PARTE
GRAVELING
OF
FLANDERS

Calais
Herring hilles
Scales elevene
PARTE
OF PICARDIE

Blacke Neser

EAST

10

THE ROUT TO THE NORTH

On the sixth day, the Armada, low on ammunition, put into Calais *(center)* to contact its land army, bottled up in Dunkirk 30 miles away. But the English sent eight flaming fireships drifting in on the crowded anchorage and the Spaniards scattered in panic. The next day the English closed in on the re-formed but tattered crescent *(top)*, driving it toward the North Sea and a long, stormy voyage home around the British Isles.

SIZE VERSUS SPEED

The Armada's flagship *San Martín,* at left, was a conventional galleon of the 16th Century. A ship of 1,200 tons, she sat high in the water with elaborate "castles" fore and aft from which infantrymen could shoot or board. Typical of the English fleet of smaller galleons and privateers of only a few hundred tons was the armed merchantman at right. Her lower castles and deeper draft gave her better speed and stability for long-range gunnery, as well as making her a smaller target. Her main deck was uncluttered by soldiers, giving the gunners working space.

141

Huge Platforms for Seaborne Cannon

By the time of the epochal Battle of Trafalgar in 1805, when Britain's brilliant admiral Horatio Nelson crushed the Franco-Spanish fleet, the concept of the ship as a gun platform had been carried to the limit of wood construction. On a big "ship of the line," more than 100 cannon were crammed onto five decks, providing devastating firepower.

But such vessels had their drawbacks. No less than 900 men were needed to man the guns and to work the towering clouds of sail necessary to move the ship. To prevent fatal strain the hulls had to have heavy longitudinal timbers, iron knees and cross bracing between the ribs. Just to steer Nelson's 226-foot, 2,200-ton flagship *Victory* took four men at the wheel—eight in rough weather. But as weapons of war, *Victory* and her sister ships were formidable in this last great battle of wooden fleets.

PORTRAIT OF A SMASHER
The biggest weapon used at Trafalgar was the short-range carronade, or "smasher," which heaved 68 pounds of iron in one blast. A forerunner of modern guns, it had a recoil slide, and could be elevated and trained in a wide arc.

FIGHTING TO THE FINISH
This diorama at England's National Maritime Museum shows the free-for-all that raged for three hours after Nelson's 27 ships broke the Franco-Spanish line at Trafalgar, near Gibraltar. *Victory* is at left center, enveloped in smoke.

Toe to toe with the *Virginia*—better known to history by her former name *Merrimack*—the little *Monitor* fires point-blank in a vain attempt to

Steam, Iron and the Turret Gun

The U.S. Civil War saw a major advance in naval warfare. On the morning of March 8, 1862, a barnlike Confederate ironclad, built up from the wooden hull of the steam frigate *Merrimack* and rechristened the *Virginia*, steamed sluggishly out of Norfolk to break the Union blockade. Though numerically outgunned, she sank two wooden warships with her iron ram and exploding shells from her new rifled cannon. The furious broadsides from her victims clanged off her sloping, greased armor with little effect.

The following day the Union sprang its own surprise: the all-iron *Monitor*, the famous "cheese box on a raft." In a four-hour gunnery duel, much of it fought at 40 yards or less, neither ship could do more than dent the other's armor. *Monitor* put a stop to *Merrimack*'s depredations. But to naval observers the battle had far greater significance for the future. Three lessons were clear: *Merrimack*'s explosive shells were devastating, armor made a ship almost impregnable, and *Monitor*'s revolving turret rendered the fixed broadside obsolete.

"MONITOR" TAKES A BREAK
Crewmen of the *Monitor* relax on the deck of their revolutionary ironclad. Behind them is the big turret, which protected her two 11-inch smoothbore cannon with eight layers of one-inch iron plate. Connected to an auxiliary steam engine that turned it a full 360°, the turret was roofed with an iron grate for ventilation and was shaded to serve as a cruising bridge.

pierce the enemy's armor—two crisscrossed layers of flattened iron rails. This diorama is at the Mariners Museum in Newport News, Virginia.

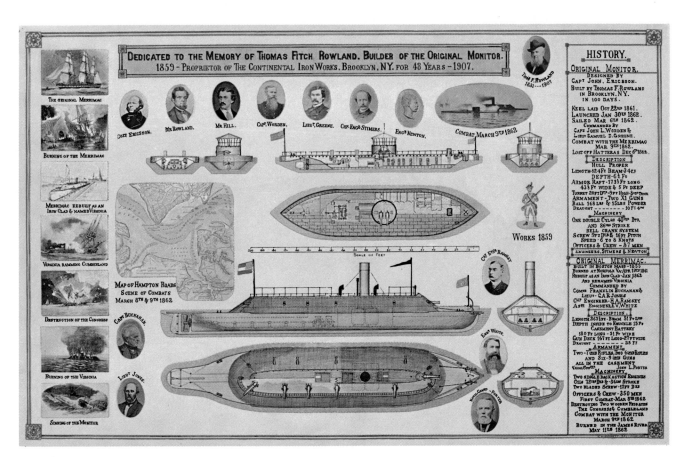

TWO PIONEERS COMPARED

This 1908 engraving contrasts the histories and specifications of the *Monitor* and *Merrimack.* At upper left is John Ericsson, the Swedish-born inventor who helped develop the propeller and designed the highly original *Monitor.* His ship's iron hull with its overhanging armored deck was 172 feet long; the 140-ton gun turret rested on a spindle extending to the keel. *Monitor's* low freeboard offered a poor target but also made her unseaworthy; she eventually sank in a gale *(lower left). Merrimack,* threatened with capture, was sunk by her captain in May 1862.

CROSSING THE GERMAN "T"

This diorama of the Battle of Jutland, at the Deutscher Marinebund memorial in Laboe, depicts the British Grand Fleet *(foreground)* as it attempted to "cross the T." The purpose of this classic maneuver was to bring the tremendous firepower of all the dreadnoughts' broadsides to bear on the enemy's lead ships *(background)*, which could reply with only a few forward guns. The Germans quickly reversed course under cover of a smoke screen and torpedo attacks by their destroyers *(upper left)*. Later that night they escaped back to base.

A WELL-ARMED BATTLEWAGON
The British flagship at Jutland was the *Iron Duke,* shown here in a model. Her main armament consisted of 10 big guns, paired in five main turrets, that could hurl 13.5-inch diameter, 3,000-pound shells about eight miles. She also had six-inch guns, used to repel destroyer torpedo attacks. *Iron Duke,* built in 1914, survived Jutland and was finally scrapped in 1946.

The Day of the Dreadnought

In the 40 years that followed the famous duel of the American ironclads, improvements in guns, armor, engines and hull design came so fast that many new ships were destined for the scrap heap by the time they were commissioned. Then on February 10, 1906, there was launched a 526-foot marvel of steel that dominated the course of naval architecture for almost 35 years. H.M.S. *Dreadnought* displaced an unheard-of 20,000 tons, mounted ten 12-inch guns, was protected by steel armor almost a foot thick, and was driven by giant turbines at nearly 22 knots.

Dreadnought fever swept the major nations in a battleship-building race that helped to bring on World War I, and continued until World War II. But in practical terms the dreadnought's day ended in 1916 at the Battle of Jutland in the North Sea, the first and last time fleets led by battleships met each other in full-scale surface action. Jutland saw the confrontation of the cream of the British and German fleets, a total of 254 ships that included 44 dreadnoughts. For 12 hours the fleets maneuvered, their big guns hurling devastating salvos as far as 20,000 yards. But the speed, firepower and numbers of ships outstripped their admirals' ability to see, communicate and control them. Moreover, neither side dared risk its big vessels at destroyer torpedo range. Though the Germans claimed victory, sinking 14 ships to 11 lost, their fleet remained bottled up by the British fleet—and, significantly, they turned to submarine warfare.

War On, Over and Under the Sea

In World War II the fears of Jutland were substantiated: the battleship was vulnerable not only to the torpedo but to the bomb as well. British aircraft helped sink the German *Tirpitz* and *Bismarck;* Japanese planes destroyed the British capital ships *Prince of Wales* and *Repulse.* Now the decisive role passed to the warships that could deliver aerial and undersea weapons most effectively: the aircraft carrier and the submarine.

In the Atlantic, German U-boats ranged from Murmansk to the Caribbean, torpedoing 14.5 million tons of Allied shipping. Only complicated countermeasures stopped them: convoys guarded by fast escort vessels carrying depth charges, radar and underwater detection devices; patrol bombers; escort carriers and destroyers in hunter-killer groups.

In the Pacific, control of the sea was wrested from the Japanese by the aircraft carrier, a highly mobile plane-launching platform that could stay at sea for months at a time. A carrier's 80 planes could deliver tons of bombs and torpedoes with accuracy at ranges up to 300 miles. So much did carriers change naval strategy that at the Battles of Midway and the Coral Sea, the first major Japanese defeats, not a single surface vessel sighted an enemy vessel.

BATTLE OF THE ATLANTIC, 1943
In this diorama at the Naval Historical Display Center in Washington, D.C., U.S. Navy forces team up against a German U-boat which has torpedoed one of a convoy of merchant ships. Sonar-equipped destroyers in the foreground have dropped 300-pound depth charges and smaller "hedgehog" projectiles which explode on contact. Overhead, laden with more depth charges, is a bomber with fighter escort from the carrier in the background, as well as a land-based patrol bomber and a sub-spotting blimp.

7

The Navigator's Ancient Skills

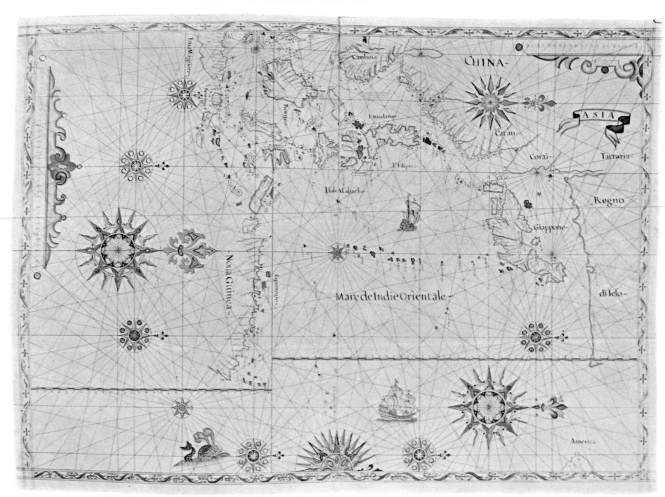

A GENOESE CHART PUBLISHED IN 1652 AND USED BY EUROPEAN NAVIGATORS OF THE TIME SHOWS WHAT WAS THEN KNOWN OF THE EAST INDIES. NORTH IS TO THE RIGHT.

A CAPTAIN NAVIGATING A SHIP at sea must constantly know the answers to certain vital questions: Where am I? Where have steam and compass, shift of wind, set of current, fetch and force of wave combined to place me and my ship on the face of the globe? What course do we steer from here to arrive safely and on time in our destined harbor?

Marine navigation—getting a ship from here to there across the sea—is usually divided into four branches, any combination or all of which may be used in a port-to-port passage. First comes piloting. In piloting the navigator figures out where he is simply by looking at various visible landmarks, perhaps listening for helpful sounds such as a bell buoy or foghorn, and steering his course accordingly. He may use objects on the shore or he may use any of the numerous buoys and other navigation aids that are found in coastal waters.

Next is dead reckoning, a term which comes from a contraction of the word "deduced" = "ded." A course is laid out on a chart, and then the navigator estimates how far along that course he has traveled since he last estimated his position. If helmsmen could steer absolutely straight courses, and if vessels could proceed at constant speeds, and if there were no such thing as currents or waves to carry a ship off her course, then dead reckoning would be all a navigator required. However, all these other elements do enter in, and the longer a ship is allowed to proceed under dead reckoning alone the more certain it is that her navigator's calculations will be in error. In short, some kind of check or reference point is needed from time to time.

Such a check is provided by the third kind of navigation—celestial—in which one's position is determined by reference to the position of the sun, moon or stars. Finally, there is electronic navigation, or plotting position with the help of signals from radio transmitters, radar equipment and other electronic devices.

The early mariner was half astrologer—sighting the stars with his strange staffs and astrolabe, timing their sidereal sweep with sandglasses —and half poet, responsive to the winging of birds, to the look of distant cloud, to the angle of wind across the face of the sea.

The ancient navigator probed the bottom with sounding pole and tallow-tipped lead and line, and learned to estimate his position accordingly. "When you get 11 fathoms and ooze on the lead," noted Herodotus in the Fourth Century B.C., "you are a day's journey from Alexandria." In other words, "When you have come so close to the African coast that the water is only 11 fathoms deep, and if at the same time the sticky tallow smeared on your sounding lead picks up a certain kind of mud, then you are close to Alexandria." Such knowledge was vital. A ship sailing south from Greece in a strong following wind might run right into the breakers and wreck herself among the coastal rocks during foggy or stormy weather unless the captain knew about where he was, and had some way of anticipating the approach to shore.

As primitive sailors ventured beyond sight of land, or perhaps were blown to sea and lost there, they turned to other aids. Floki Vilgjerdarsson, the great Norwegian explorer who was one of the first to take a Viking ship from Norway to Iceland, was sometimes called Ravna-Floki (Raven-Floki) because he took caged ravens on his voyages and released them when he figured land was near. If they circled above the ship, then returned to the deck, he fared on; no land was in sight. But if they winged away with purpose and conviction, he set his course to follow them, knowing they would lead him to a landfall.

Navigating by clouds, scents and waves

Other signs, other portents, guided men and their flimsy craft. Island cumuli, for instance—high, white castles of convection clouds rising from heated land masses—proclaimed the presence of unseen atolls below the horizon. Also, land had distinctive smells that evening breezes carried as much as 30 or 50 miles to sea: the scent of orange blossoms, of grass, the aroma of burning wood. And though the methods of Polynesian and Micronesian navigators were tribal secrets, we know now that they could read wave and eddy patterns created by islands hundreds of miles away, and that they could home in on them as accurately as if they were cruising down a radio direction beam.

This was the essence of the so-called art of navigation as practiced by early navigators, most of whom were realistic enough to understand that no matter what magic isles they found, merely to discover them was only part of the task: they must know how to set a course for home and, just as important, how to sail back to the islands again. So what the mariner needed was not art but science. He needed a body of knowledge about the physical characteristics, the geometry, of his world, and intimations of some kind of dependable order or system related to the mechanics of his universe.

Pythagoras gave shape to the earth in the Sixth Century B.C. when he proclaimed it round. Two hundred years later both Aristotle and Plato reasserted his belief. Within another century, Eratosthenes, the brilliant Alexandrian, gave it dimension. About 25,000 miles around, he figured it, in a flight of mathematical creativity that still glows with stunning elegance. (Today, 23 centuries later, we make it 24,902.) Eratosthenes observed that the sun at high noon on the day of the summer solstice, when it reached its farthest point north in its annual weaving back and forth across the equator, shone directly down a well at Syene (modern Aswan), and therefore was directly overhead. But he knew also that at this same moment, in Alexandria some 500 miles to the north, the sun cast a shadow. The angle made by the sun's rays in casting a shadow at Alexandria, he reasoned, must correspond exactly to the angle subtended at the earth's center by the two towns on its surface—Syene and Alexandria. He found the angle at Alexandria to equal about 7.2°, or about 1/50 of a sphere's 360°. Therefore the 500 miles that separated the towns must equal 1/50 of the circumference, or "great circle" measurement, of the earth. Answer: 50 × 500 miles, or 25,000 miles.

In the Second Century A.D., the Egyptian genius Claudius Ptolemy

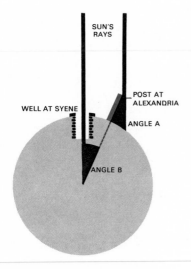

THE SIZE OF THE EARTH was determined by the Greek mathematician Eratosthenes in 240 B.C., 17 centuries before Magellan first circumnavigated it. Eratosthenes discovered that on a day when the sun's rays were shining directly down into a well in Syene, Egypt, they were hitting a post 500 miles away in Alexandria at an angle of 7.2°. He knew by geometry that the angle (A) equaled an angle between two imaginary lines drawn from the earth's center to Alexandria and Syene. Since 7.2° is 1/50 of a circle, he reckoned that the distance from Syene to Alexandria was 1/50 the earth's circumference. Multiplication produced a figure of 25,000 miles for the earth's girth—correct within 100 miles.

gave new form and substance to the world, portraying what was known of it on his famous maps, describing it in his books on geography and cosmography. Ptolemy's world reached from the British Isles and the west coast of Africa as far east as China, and from about the Arctic Circle in the north to a line well below the equator running through Africa and the Indian Ocean. Most important for the development of navigational science, however, Ptolemy laid down lines on his maps. These were the first terrestrial coordinates, the *parallels* of latitude and the *meridians* of longitude—indispensable for locating a ship on the face of the globe.

With this concept—the division of the earth's spherical surface into geometrical coordinates—the science of navigation was provided with a foundation, a basic language: the degrees and minutes of the great circles of longitude that converge on the poles like lines separating the segments of an orange; the degrees and minutes of the circles of latitude that girdle the earth like belts, becoming smaller as they get farther from the equator. With longitude for determining locations east and west, and latitude for ascertaining distance north and south, it was now theoretically possible to locate one's position at sea with scientific certitude and accuracy. If a mariner could correctly establish his east-west line of position and his north-south line of position, he knew his ship would be where the two lines intersected.

The *Odyssey* and the stars

For thousands of years before Ptolemy, mariners had steered by the stars. Book V of the *Odyssey* tells how Ulysses set sail from Kalypso's isle, and set his course by the Pleiades, the Plowman, the Great Bear and Orion.

> *These stars the beautiful Kalypso bade him*
> *hold on his left hand as he crossed the main.*

This method, while it may have worked for daring literary heroes like Ulysses (who also had the gods to help him when he got lost), was not accurate enough for most ancient mariners when they ventured far from land. Most stars do not hold still in the sky but appear to go careening across it in great curves every night as the earth turns. Sailors needed something steadier to steer by, and they found it in certain stars like Polaris, which do not appear to move. Polaris is almost directly due north of the axis of the earth's rotation. As a result, when the earth turns, Polaris, instead of racing across the sky, appears to move in such a tiny circle that to all intents and purposes it is stationary in the heavens.

With such a reference point, mariners could begin making a pretty fair estimate of how far north or south they were on the earth's surface by measuring the star's "altitude." Altitude, or elevation, is a measurement of the angle that a celestial body makes with the horizon, and is calculated in degrees. To visualize this, one should imagine the sky as forming a smooth round bowl over his head and coming down to the

150 A.D.

1000 A.D.

THE GEOGRAPHY OF THE WORLD was better known at the close of antiquity, about 150 A.D. *(green area, top drawing)*, than it was some 900 years later in the Middle Ages *(bottom)*. Ancient scholars diligently inquired into the size and shape of the earth and drew maps from reports by the armies of Alexander the Great and Roman traders with the East. Scientific inquiry languished during the Middle Ages and though Norse explorers got to Greenland and beyond, knowledge of parts of Africa and the East was forgotten.

horizon all around him. Looking out toward the horizon, his eye follows a nearly horizontal line parallel with the earth's surface. Looking straight up, his eye follows a vertical line. Since the angle between those horizontal and vertical lines is 90°, a star directly overhead would be said to have an altitude of 90°, and one on the horizon would have an elevation of zero degrees. Standing in Minneapolis and looking at Polaris, the North Star, an observer sees that it is about halfway between horizon and zenith, and he gives it an elevation of 45°. However, if he were to go south to the equator the North Star would appear almost on the horizon. Proceeding farther south still, he would not be able to see the North Star at all; it would have disappeared below the horizon.

This useful characteristic of a pole star was noticed by early mariners. Logically, and correctly, they figured that all they had to do to maintain a steady course to the east or west was to make sure the star remained the same distance above the horizon night after night. Moreover, once they knew the latitude of a certain island, it became a relatively simple matter to sail there again and again. They merely sailed north (or south) until the pole star appeared at the proper distance above the horizon. They made a right-angle turn, and sailed due west (or east), keeping the star at the same elevation, confident that sooner or later that would raise the landfall they sought.

Taking a position with the fingers

Today, to calculate the elevation of Polaris, a navigator uses a sextant, a kind of protractor equipped with mirrors and lenses. Holding this to his eye, he can simultaneously sight on the horizon and the star, and measure their angular relationship by taking a reading from a scale on the sextant itself. But 3,000 years ago Phoenician navigators were probably gauging the pole star's altitude with extended arm and spread fingers: little finger on the horizon, thumb to the zenith. Pytheas of Massalia (Marseilles), the great Greek navigator and astronomer, who sailed north to Scotland and Thule in the Fourth Century B.C., may have used a *gnomon*, a vertical stick or rod with which he could calculate the sun's elevation at noon by the length of the shadow it cast; from this, allowing for the time of the year, he could make a rough estimate of his latitude.

As centuries passed, astronomers—Arabian, Italian, English—invented more sophisticated and ever more accurate instruments for measuring the altitude of celestial bodies. Among the many such instruments used were the sea astrolabe (from the Greek "star taker") and the cross-staff. The astrolabe, possibly invented by Hipparchus about 150 B.C., consisted of a movable pointer fixed to the center of a wood or metal disk whose circumference was marked off in degrees. By sighting the celestial body along the pointer and then taking a reading on the disk of the degrees, the navigator could determine the altitude of the star or planet. In the 15th Century, the cross-staff came into general use. Attached at right angles to a straight staff about 36 inches long and bearing a scale of degrees was a shorter crosspiece which could be moved up and down the staff. A small hole was bored at each end of the crosspiece. To get the altitude of a heavenly body, the navigator sighted along the staff and moved the crosspiece until he could see the star through one hole and the horizon through the other. He then took his reading from the location of the crosspiece on the scaled staff. The sextant—which with refinements is still in use today—was independently invented in England and the United States in the 18th Century.

As early as the 15th Century, considerable strides were taken in organizing the science of navigation by the establishment of a kind of advanced study institute near the village of Sagres in Portugal. The man behind this project was Portugal's Prince Henry, now known as Henry the Navigator. Despite all these efforts, the location of position at sea was still rather haphazard. Trying to hold the crude predecessors of the sextant steady on the deck of a pitching ship made the getting of an accurate sight almost a lucky accident. By Magellan's time, in the 1520s, although astronomers and mathematicians could determine latitudes within half a degree of accuracy, a pilot at sea considered himself fortunate to come within five degrees of his true position.

The one indispensable navigating instrument of every mariner at that time was his magnetic compass—a magnetized needle, swinging freely on a pivot so that it could point to the north. Where and when it was first used is not known. It may have been in China in the 10th Century, or England in the 11th—there are no records. However it was certainly in general use by the 1300s, and probably well before that. The only trouble with early compasses was that they did not always work as they should. In certain parts of the world, and even on certain vessels, the needle would point stubbornly several degrees in the wrong direction. The trouble, of course, came from two conditions now known as *variation* and *deviation*.

The two north poles

Variation arises from the fact that true north and magnetic north are not the same. True north is at the north pole, a spot in the middle of the Arctic Ocean. Magnetic north is determined by the magnetic field of the earth itself, and is in northeastern Canada about 1,000 miles from true north. The needle normally points to magnetic north, and thus will show a greater or lesser error, depending on where the compass reading is taken. A reading taken from far to the south—down on the equator or in the Southern Hemisphere—will show a fairly small variation, since at that distance the magnetic-north and true-north poles will seem close together. And, of course, if the compass happens to be in line with the two poles, there will be no variation at all. But in New England, the angle between the two is fairly large (about 14 degrees). Variation is further complicated by the fact that the magnetic pole wanders slowly around and a yearly correction must also be applied.

Deviation, while less mysterious, is often more troublesome. On wooden craft, it came from the presence of iron objects in the ship itself, like nails or cannon barrels. This problem of deviation was partially solved by an English navigator, Captain Matthew Flinders, who worked out a way of placing one or more small bars of soft iron near the compass, locating them in such a way as to cancel out deviation errors. Since most modern ships are themselves made of metal, additional devices are needed to make their compasses work accurately. One commonly used is comprised of two large balls of iron, one on each side of the compass. They are located so close to the needle, and their pull is so strong that they counteract each other, blot out the pull of certain kinds of iron in the ship, and enable the compass to function normally.

Converting time into distance

The next most essential instrument—some navigators might even put it alongside the compass in importance—is, surprisingly enough, a good clock. A clock is indispensable in finding one's longitude, since the problem here is one of time—figuring how many hours the ship has traveled east or west of the zero meridian at Greenwich, England. To understand this, consider a hypothetical at-sea situation. A ship is in mid-Atlantic. In the middle of the day the navigator begins taking a series of sights on the sun, to determine the exact moment of noon, i.e., that moment when the sun reaches maximum altitude at this point on the earth's surface. He immediately looks at his chronometer, which is an extremely accurate clock set to coincide with the time at Greenwich. The chronometer says 2:30, so the navigator knows he is two and a half hours west of Greenwich. Since the earth makes a complete rotation (or 360°) in 24 hours, it will turn 15° in one hour. In two and a half hours it will turn 37½°, and so the ship's position is 37° and 30 minutes west longitude.

But during the great Age of Discovery of the 15th and 16th Centuries, pilots and mariners had few mechanical timepieces of any description, let alone an accurate chronometer. Instead, they kept track of time as best they could by means of half-hour sandglasses. Every half hour, as the last of the sand ran out, a man on watch turned it over; he struck a bell for each turn since the beginning of the watch, usually a period of four hours. The practice still survives on shipboard and explains nautical timekeeping by "bells"—one bell for 12:30, two bells for 1 o'clock, three bells for 1:30, and so on, up to eight bells for 4 o'clock, when a new watch begins and the count starts over.

As for distance sailed east or west, early mariners relied solely on dead reckoning, estimating their speed by peering over the side and noting the rate at which foam slipped past the planking. The results they came up with were little more than a compound of hunch, guesswork and intuition. Samuel Eliot Morison calculates that on Columbus' first Atlantic passage, he consistently overestimated the distance of his day's run by about 9 per cent, which scales up to a 90-mile error for every 1,000 miles traveled. However, the remarkable fact is not how far off these navigators were, but how amazingly close they came using such primitive methods.

Progress in the following centuries came slowly. In the late 1500s, some ingenious mariner—name and nationality unknown—invented the common, or chip, log, a simple speed-measuring device. The chip log was a piece of wood shaped like a slice of pie. Attached to it was a light line, knotted at certain equal intervals. To check the ship's speed, a man threw the log overboard, turned a small 30-second sandglass, and began counting the knots that slipped through his fingers as the ship left the log astern. The number of knots he counted in 30 seconds was translated into the nautical miles per hour his ship was traveling. With this device began usage of the term "knots" to mean "nautical miles per hour."

During the 16th and 17th Centuries scientists made many improvements in charts and instruments but because there was still no reliable clock, an accurate system for determining longitude continued to evade astronomers and navigators alike. And it was proving costly. In 1707, 2,000 men drowned in a single disaster when a squadron of British ships ran aground in the fog because it had miscalculated its longitude. Seven years later, in desperation, Parliament established a Board of Longitude and authorized it to pay the then staggering sum of £20,000 to the man who devised a means of determining longitude whose error, after six weeks of sailing, would not exceed 30 miles, an average error of less than three seconds of time a day. John Harrison, a Yorkshire cabinetmaker, set out to capture the fabulous prize. He submitted his Chronometer No. 1 to the Board in 1735, when he was 42. Spring-activated, utilizing different metals to compensate for temperature changes, and weighing 72 pounds, it was tried out at sea with remarkable success. It lost about four minutes in three weeks. The Board awarded Harrison £500 and encouraged him to continue his work.

The prizewinning clock

In 1761, Harrison's No. 4 chronometer sailed aboard H.M.S. *Deptford* for Jamaica. On arrival after a six-weeks' passage, the instrument was five seconds slow. On its return to England several months later, its total loss was 1 minute, 54½ seconds, well within the prize limit. In 1772, the famous Captain James Cook took a duplicate of No. 4 with him on his voyage to the Antarctic. It functioned perfectly in the sub-zero weather. "Our never-failing guide . . .," Cook called it. A year later, the Board paid Harrison in full for his half-a-lifetime of work. Ever since, chronometers have been standard equipment on oceangoing ships.

Modern ships have sophisticated electronic gear that provides navigating information of remarkable accuracy. There is, for example, an electronic echo sounder which bounces sound waves off the ocean floor, times the return of the echo and, from this information, reveals the contour of the bottom and the depth of the water. In the blackest night, a radarscope on the bridge yields the range and bearing of any sizable object up to 40 or 50 miles away. To give a ship its bearing when she is within range of a transmitter, there is the worldwide RDF (Radio Direction Finder). A sensitive loop antenna on the vessel picks up a radio

AN ACCURATE CHRONOMETER, essential for finding longitude at sea, was first developed by British cabinetmaker John Harrison, who built a series of five clocks from 1735 to 1771. The one shown here had an intricate spring and balance mechanism *(above)* and three dials *(below)* for seconds, minutes and hours. Harrison could not test this model at sea because England was at war with Spain and the Government dared not risk its capture.

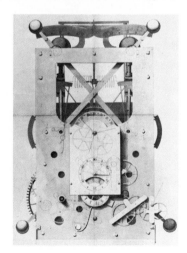

directional beam from a land-based transmitter operating on a known frequency, and from that signal, the captain learns his course or line of position. With loran (long-range navigation), effective for some 700 to 1,400 miles offshore, the ship receives synchronized, intersecting radio signals which give a position accurate within a tenth of a mile.

In addition to constant improvements in these systems, even more spectacular navigation aids are being introduced. In one, specially programmed shipboard computers process data from the Navy's three navigational satellites, and in less than one second give the vessel's position with great accuracy. The system is worldwide and operates in all weather. Also under development is bathymetric navigation equipment which enables a captain to locate his position by echo soundings over a previously surveyed and electronically mapped area of ocean floor. Scientists foresee strip maps of thousands of miles of ocean floor under the major sea-lanes to give the navigator identifiable landfalls *beneath* the water.

However, most seamen are a wary lot, and they like to supplement new devices with the old, tried-and-true procedures that have stood them in good stead in many a tight situation in years gone by. A sextant, a magnetic compass and a chronometer are still aboard every ship that goes to sea.

The Art of Getting There

If the average landlubber should suddenly find himself at the helm of a small boat, he would probably become hopelessly lost in a world of blank seas and mysterious coastlines. But to an experienced navigator the sea is as well marked as a superhighway. All that is needed is practice, a few instruments, navigational tables—and, above all else, a nautical chart. A chart is a sort of oceanic road map describing everything a navigator needs to know about a particular patch of sea: water depth, hazards to shipping, compass variation, currents, buoys, lighthouses, landmarks and other invaluable information. The following pages trace the progress of a small boat, the *Sheila Anne,* as she voyages from Wellfleet on Cape Cod to Yarmouth, Nova Scotia, a journey requiring knowledge of buoys, celestial and electronic navigation and piloting—in short, all the navigational problems that a small-boat sailor would be likely to face on any short sea voyage.

INSTRUMENTS OF DIRECTION
A nautical chart, with the course from Cape Cod to Nova Scotia marked in red, is decked with navigation tools. From top: a compass; parallel rules for drawing directional lines on the chart; dividers for computing distances; a protractor for measuring angles; a sextant for measuring the angle between a heavenly body and the horizon, and a Nautical Almanac, a book of navigational tables.

Sheila Anne's wake curves smoothly around a nun buoy as she follows a bend in the channel heading out of Wellfleet Harbor. The buoy, its

Signposts of the Sea

On the first leg of her voyage, *Sheila Anne* leaves Wellfleet Harbor and heads for Cape Cod Bay. (The red line on the small chart at left and on those on the following pages show the progress of the voyage.) Cruising in such shallow, crowded waters can be very tricky unless a skipper knows how to read the buoys. For instance, the chart shows that the buoy pictured above marks a shoal only two feet deep at low tide; sailors who fail to keep the buoy to their left as they leave the harbor will run aground.

After passing the buoy at the end of treacherous Billingsgate Island, which lurks beneath the surface at high tide, the boat follows a compass course of 268° *(red lines on chart, right)*. Since a small boat's compass points to magnetic, not geographic, north, the course is computed from the inner, or magnetic, circle on the chart's red compass "rose." When *Sheila Anne* passes C "1," she turns northward to 358°, a course that should lead her to the tip of Cape Cod and the edge of the Atlantic.

THE LANGUAGE OF THE BUOYS

Buoys and their chart symbols *(both shown at right)* are to a mariner what traffic signs and road maps are to a motorist: they tell him where he is and warn him of dangers. Black buoys, marked with odd numbers, show the left side of a channel as a ship returns from sea, and red, even-numbered buoys mark the right side, or the return—hence the mariner's rule-of-thumb, "Red, Right, Returning." Cylindrical "can" buoys come in various colors and patterns, depending upon their function; conical "nuns" are usually red. Larger buoys have gongs, lights, bells and whistles, often in combinations. A black-and-red horizontally striped buoy means that the water on either side is navigable, but that the side indicated by the top color is preferred. There are some 23,000 buoys in U.S. waters, serviced by buoy tenders of the U.S. Coast Guard.

BLACK CAN BUOY
(ODD-NUMBERED)

RED NUN BUOY
(EVEN-NUMBERED)

ANCHORAGE BUOY
(MARKS ANCHORAGE AREA)

MID-CHANNEL BUOY
(EITHER SIDE NAVIGABLE)

GONG BUOY
(ACTIVATED BY WAVES)

LIGHTED BUOY
(POWERED BY BATTERIES)

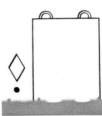

LIGHTED BELL BUOY
(ACTIVATED BY WAVES)

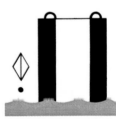

LIGHTED WHISTLE BUOY
(ACTIVATED BY WAVES)

conical top designed to be a radar reflector, is designated N ''12,'' and can be found on the chart below between Indian Neck and Great Island.

This is a portion of the Wellfleet Harbor chart. The small numbers show depth in feet at average low tide. Blue water is less than 13 feet deep.

TAKING A BEARING

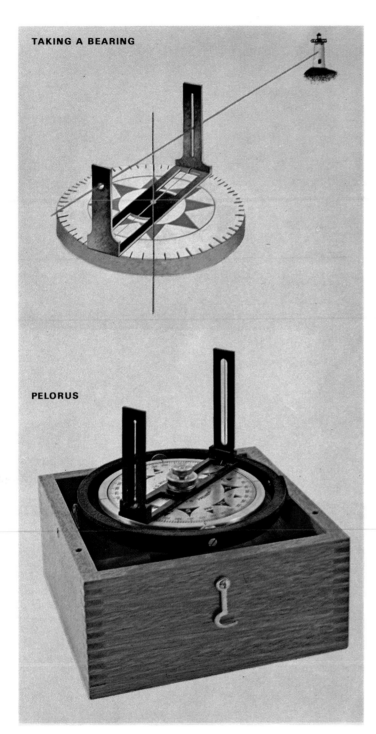

PELORUS

A magnetic compass points to the magnetic north pole, which is about 1,000 miles from the geographic, or true, north pole. In the top diagram, which shows a boat's outline on a compass rose, the difference between the two norths, or compass variation, is 15° 45′ (minutes) west; that is, magnetic north, from that point on earth, bears 15° 45′ west of true north. So the magnetic reading 351° *(bottom)* equals 335° 15′ true. The fixed vertical mark on the compass (called a "lubber's line") is parallel to the boat's keel and shows her heading.

TRUE AND MAGNETIC NORTH

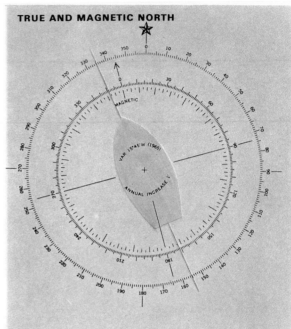

MAGNETIC STEERING COMPASS

BEARINGS WITH A "DUMB COMPASS"

Large ships have extra compasses especially designed for taking bearings, but on a boat that has only a steering compass, bearings are taken with a pelorus *(above)*. Called a "dumb compass" because it is not magnetized, it consists of two sighting vanes and a circular card divided into 360 degrees—identical to a real compass card. To take a bearing on an object, the skipper turns the pelorus card until it is aligned with his steering compass, so that north is on the same position on each card. Now he turns the vanes until he can sight the object through them. He reads the bearing on the card through the space beneath the vane nearest the object.

Fixing an Error by Getting a Fix

The 358° course plotted on the previous page should have led *Sheila Anne* straight to the buoy at the tip of Cape Cod. But wind and current, as well as human error, can easily carry a ship off course. Therefore, a navigator must frequently check his position, or "get a fix."

If the ship is in sight of land, the first step in getting a fix is finding a landmark and identifying it on the chart. Then the navigator uses his pelorus *(far left)* to determine the landmark's direction—or bearing—

from the ship. Most fixes, like the one explained below, are obtained with bearings on two landmarks, but if more are in sight, they can be used for additional accuracy. Even on big ships replete with sophisticated electronic equipment, visual bearings are still considered the most reliable way to get a fix.

Sheila Anne's fix shows that she is headed far west of where she should be. She changes course to 018° to reach the buoy, beyond which is the sea—and new navigation problems.

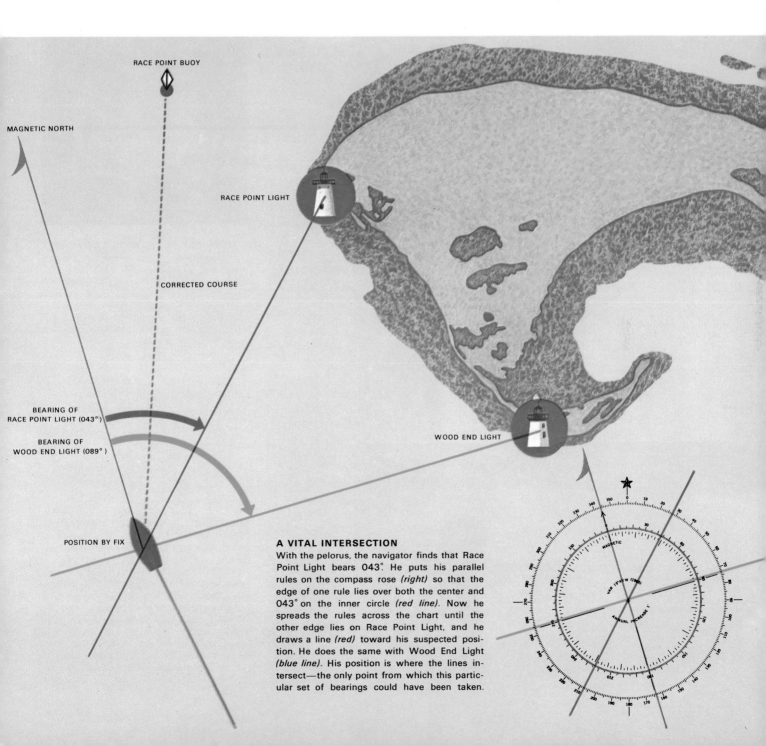

RACE POINT BUOY

MAGNETIC NORTH

CORRECTED COURSE

RACE POINT LIGHT

WOOD END LIGHT

BEARING OF
RACE POINT LIGHT (043°)

BEARING OF
WOOD END LIGHT (089°)

POSITION BY FIX

A VITAL INTERSECTION

With the pelorus, the navigator finds that Race Point Light bears 043°. He puts his parallel rules on the compass rose *(right)* so that the edge of one rule lies over both the center and 043° on the inner circle *(red line)*. Now he spreads the rules across the chart until the other edge lies on Race Point Light, and he draws a line *(red)* toward his suspected position. He does the same with Wood End Light *(blue line)*. His position is where the lines intersect—the only point from which this particular set of bearings could have been taken.

Seeking the Help of the Sun

Sheila Anne's navigator is now far from land, out of sight of any helpful landmarks. But he can get a good idea of where he is by using the sun to find a "line of position." The principle involved is shown in the diagram at right. A single sun sighting is like getting a bearing on one landmark: it tells the navigator only that he is somewhere on the resulting line. But he usually has enough of a notion about his position so he can tell approximately where on the line he is. Or he can wait an hour or so, until the sun is at a different angle, and then find another line of position. The intersection of the two lines of position, with the boat's course and speed taken into account, gives him a fairly accurate "running fix."

To find a line of position, a navigator needs three things: a sextant, a chronometer and navigational tables. These tables, compiled and issued by the U.S. Navy, are an indispensable source of information, containing all the data the navigator needs to make the complex computations involved.

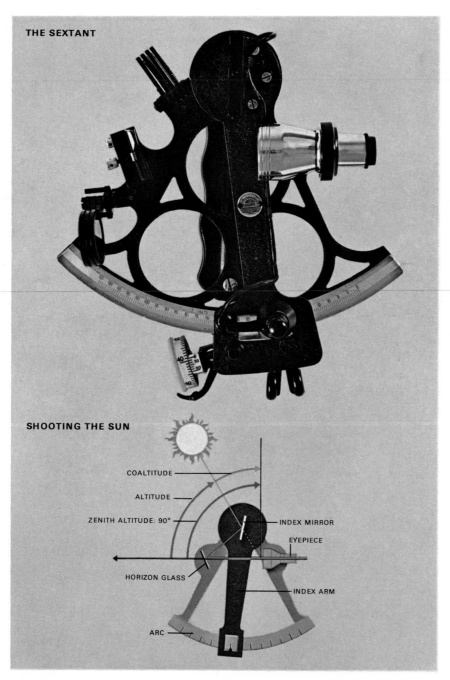

THE SEXTANT

SHOOTING THE SUN

COALTITUDE

ALTITUDE

ZENITH ALTITUDE: 90°

HORIZON GLASS

ARC

INDEX MIRROR

EYEPIECE

INDEX ARM

A TIMEPIECE SET FOR ENGLAND
The chronometer is an extremely accurate clock used to establish the exact time of a celestial observation. It is set to Greenwich (England) time, because that is the standard time given in all nautical tables. Precision is vital, since a few seconds' error in time can result in an error of miles in a ship's position.

SHOOTING THE SUN WITH A SEXTANT
To use a sextant, the navigator follows the procedure illustrated at left. He first sights the horizon *(black arrow)* through the horizon glass, which is half mirror. Then he moves the index mirror with the index arm until he also sees the sun, reflected from the index mirror to the horizon-glass mirror to his eye *(red line)*. He adjusts the sun's image until its bottom edge is even with the horizon. He reads the sun's altitude *(green arrow)* on the calibrated arc. Its coaltitude *(red arrow)*, necessary for finding a line of position, is found by subtracting its altitude from 90°, the altitude of the zenith *(brown arrow)*.

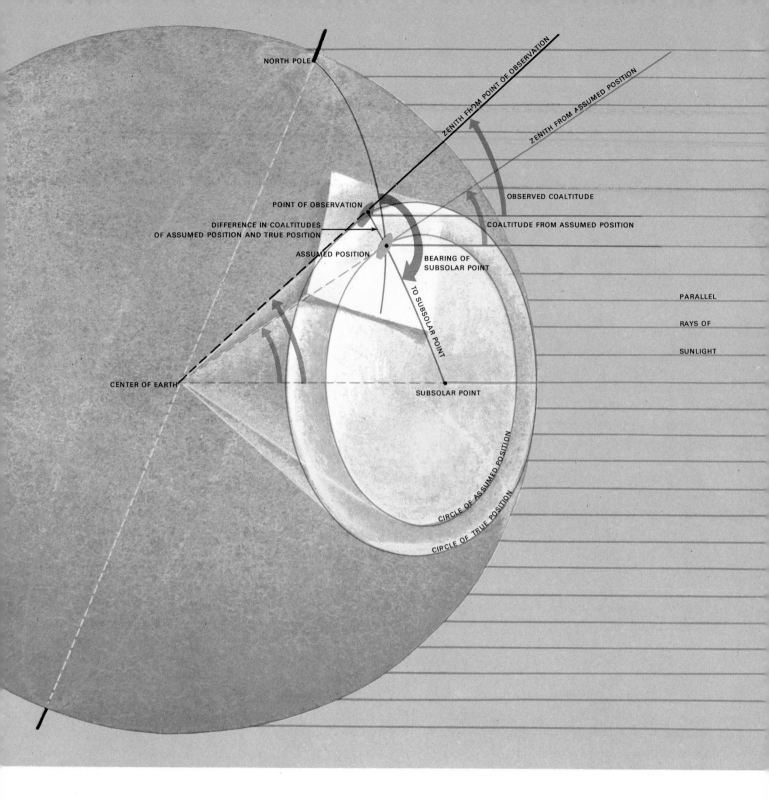

NORTH POLE

ZENITH FROM POINT OF OBSERVATION

ZENITH FROM ASSUMED POSITION

POINT OF OBSERVATION

OBSERVED COALTITUDE

DIFFERENCE IN COALTITUDES
OF ASSUMED POSITION AND TRUE POSITION

COALTITUDE FROM ASSUMED POSITION

ASSUMED POSITION

BEARING OF
SUBSOLAR POINT

TO SUBSOLAR POINT

PARALLEL

RAYS OF

SUNLIGHT

CENTER OF EARTH

SUBSOLAR POINT

CIRCLE OF ASSUMED POSITION

CIRCLE OF TRUE POSITION

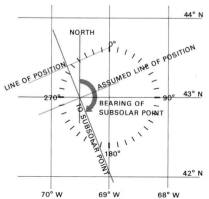

44° N

NORTH

LINE OF POSITION

0°

ASSUMED LINE OF POSITION

270°   90°   43° N

BEARING OF
SUBSOLAR POINT

TO SUBSOLAR POINT

180°

42° N

70° W   69° W   68° W

FINDING A LINE OF POSITION

There is always some point on earth where the sun is overhead—i.e., at an altitude of 90°: this is the "subsolar point." An observer elsewhere would not see the sun at the zenith, but at an angle from the zenith, called the coaltitude. The mariner "shoots the sun" with his sextant and computes its coaltitude as 30 degrees and 10 minutes (a minute is one sixtieth of a degree). Since each minute equals one nautical mile, he knows that he is somewhere on a huge circle with a radius of 1,810 miles, centered on the subsolar point—a circle so big that the part he is on is essentially a straight line. To find where that line is, he selects an assumed position,

near where he thinks he is; from his tables he finds that the subsolar point bears 158° from his assumed position. He draws a 158° line through that position *(gray arrow, left)*—in effect the spoke of a wheel. Since the angle between a spoke and the rim is always 90°, his line of position must be perpendicular to the 158° line. He consults the tables and finds that the sun's coaltitude from his assumed position, at the instant of the observation, was 30°—10 minutes less than his actual coaltitude. Hence, he is somewhere on a line of position that crosses the 158° line 10 miles farther from the subsolar point than his assumed position.

ECHO SOUNDER

TAKING A SOUNDING

Finding the Way in a Fog

With his journey nearly complete, *Sheila Anne*'s navigator is suddenly enveloped by fog that cuts visibility to a few feet. Before the advent of the electronic age, such a situation was often disastrous: a "blind" navigator, aided only by a compass and depth soundings with a lead-weighted line, had to steer his course through dangerous shoals and fickle currents primarily by guesswork.

Today, thanks largely to wartime technology, a navigator can take continuous soundings and at the same time "see" through fog to get a fix. Although such sophisticated electronic equipment as radar and loran are too expensive for most small-boat owners, an echo sounder *(left)* and a radio direction finder *(below and right)* are relatively inexpensive, and are to be found on many boats that venture out into large bodies of water.

NAVIGATING BY BEEPS AND ECHOES

An echo sounder, used to measure depth, emits sound impulses and records their echoes. The interval between each beep and its echo is translated into so many feet of depth on a dial *(top);* this reading can be compared with depth figures on a chart. It is particularly useful when the sea bottom is irregular and thus distinctive.

SEEKING THE SOURCE OF A SIGNAL

To pinpoint the source of a radio signal, the navigator rotates the antenna on top of the radio direction finder until he has found the null, or that point where the signal is at minimum strength. The white pointer perpendicular to the antenna then shows the direction of the signal.

A PAIR OF ELECTRONIC LANDMARKS

Like all light vessels, *Lurcher,* named for the shoal it is anchored over, has a light, a foghorn *(concentric circles)* and a radio beacon *(wavy lines).* Using his radio direction finder, *Sheila* *Anne*'s navigator takes the bearings of the signals from *Lurcher* and Seal Island Lighthouse and, with the same methods he used to get a visual fix, plots his position. Projecting his present course *(dotted line),* he finds he will pass to the south of *Lurcher;* since (because of the fog) he wants to find her as a further position check, he must now change his course to the north.

167

Getting Home
on the Range

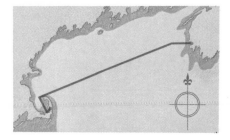

Cruising to the east from *Lurcher* lightship, *Sheila Anne* makes an evening landfall on the coast of Nova Scotia. At some point she must turn up into Yarmouth Sound, but if she changes course too soon she could wind up in Outer False Bay, or on the unmarked tip of Cape Fourchu.

The heavy clouds augur a pitch-black night, and only two lights are in sight: Cape Fourchu Light, on the peninsula between Outer False Bay and Yarmouth Sound, and Cat Rock Buoy, south of the peninsula. The navigator knows that a line between them is, in effect, the boundary between the two bodies of water. He decides to use the lights as a "range"; that is, he will stay on course until he sees the two lights in line. Only then can he turn and be sure he is safely headed up the Sound to Yarmouth.

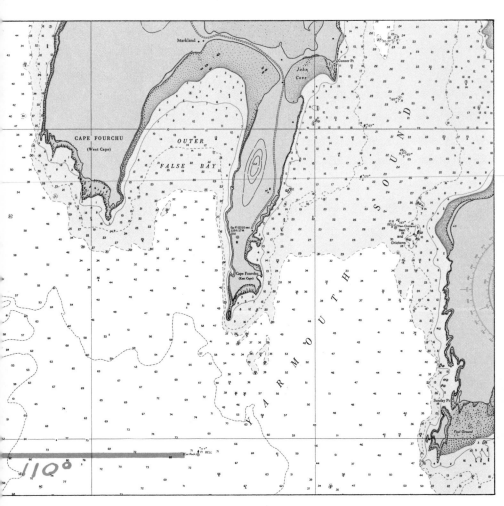

LINING UP THE LIGHTS

Nearing the lighted bell buoy identified as "11Y" on the chart, *Sheila Anne* has almost lined up the range formed by the buoy and the Cape Fourchu lighthouse. Ripples backing up from the buoy tell the navigator that a tidal current is flooding into Yarmouth Sound; it will help him on his way as he turns the buoy and sets his course for the final run up the Sound.

8
Extending the Nautical Frontiers

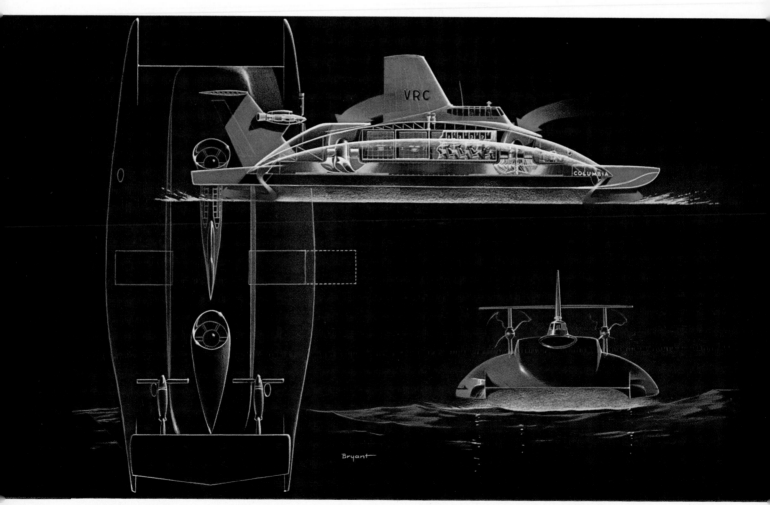

THREE VIEWS OF THE PROPOSED AIR-CUSHION VEHICLE "COLUMBIA" PROVIDE A GLIMPSE OF THE FUTURE. THE REVOLUTIONARY 100-TON SHIP IS DESIGNED TO GO 150 KNOTS.

DESIGNERS OF NEW TYPES OF SHIPS of the future have two diametrically opposite objectives. The first is the creation of craft that enable man to travel and carry cargo beneath the sea—and to explore, map and exploit the floors of the oceans as he has the land on which he lives. The second is the building of a fast transoceanic vessel with a hull that will rise completely out of the water—a sort of hybrid ship-and-airplane.

Although subsurface exploration is centuries old—daredevils are reported to have ventured beneath the Mediterranean in devices like inverted cups as long ago as 400 B.C.—man still knows little about the 329 million cubic miles of salt water that comprise the seas, or about that part of the earth which lies on the ocean bottom. A few facts are known —for example, that the world's longest mountain range and its deepest canyons are underwater. And there is some tantalizing speculation. Scientists believe that somewhere in the sea's foothills, deserts and sunken continents an untold wealth in minerals and precious stones awaits discovery, and that lakes of oil a thousand times richer than those of the Middle East are also there for the tapping. Moreover, within the seas of the world are fish and plankton—protein sufficient, if properly harvested, to feed the world. But despite its rich promise, man has explored only about 9 per cent of the bottom of the sea—mostly the continental shelves—and has mapped less than 5 per cent. This gap in man's knowledge about the oceans began to close about the 1940s, however, in response to mounting demands for raw materials, especially oil. The success of offshore oil wells and similar enterprises encouraged men to look further to the sea as a means of fulfilling the needs. Investments in underwater ventures increased. Maritime nations are now spending more than $10 billion yearly on the exploration, mapping and exploitation of the sea's resources. This amount is expected to increase by 15 per cent annually in the years ahead.

This new and intense concern with the sea has generated a whole new family of water vehicles, some of them seemingly drawn from science fiction. These include a monster oil rig that "walks" through the water on diesel-powered, steel legs; a 335-foot Floating Instrument Platform (FLIP) that is sailed to its station like a boat, then is flooded in the stern until the bow extends vertically from the water to provide a submerged platform for sensitive oceanographic instruments; and saucerlike submersibles that scan the ocean's depths with television eyes and gather specimens from the bottom with ingenious steel "hands" controlled from inside the craft.

The rapid progress made in military submarines since the success of the nuclear-powered *Nautilus* has led naval architects and engineers to give serious consideration to submarine cargo vessels. Such craft, some authorities believe, would be especially well adapted to tanker duty. A nuclear submarine tanker that could carry 40,000 tons of oil at almost 40 knots could be built today, the experts say, and would consume only about half the power of a nuclear surface ship with the same capacity and traveling at the same high speed. Such a sub might be valuable to supply naval ships in the event of war, although not for commercial use.

The underwater world is becoming familiar to laymen, too. In such craft as the Perry *Cubmarine,* two passengers can cruise for hours 50 to 100 feet beneath the surface in an enchanted, dimly lighted cosmos of seaflowers and fish. Some knowledgeable observers believe that such vessels presage an entirely new recreational era. "Mass-produced underwater vehicles," writes Athelstan Spilhaus in the *Bulletin of the Atomic Scientists,* "will become as common as automobiles. . . . Submarine trains and guided tours will take people through the reefs. . . . Underwater hunting and photography will become ever more popular sports."

Equally important advances are being made with surface craft, both in the improvement of conventional ships and in the creation of completely new breeds of "flying" vessels capable of speeds and performances no conventional ship could ever achieve.

Ships with automated controls

Among the many innovations in merchant vessels, along with the giant tanker and containerization, is the gradual introduction of mechanized engine-room controls and of automatic navigational aids. This combination may some day lead to cargo-ship crews scarcely larger than those on airplanes: a deck officer, engineer and steward on duty for each watch, or a total complement of nine or 10 men. If human judgment were not vital, it might even be possible to dispense with crews entirely and send radio-controlled robot ships across the ocean.

Other developments, no less significant, loom in propulsion systems. In the next several decades or so, the traditional oil-fired boiler may well be supplanted on many ships by nuclear power, which is already considered as momentous an advance over conventional steam as conventional steam was over sail. The potential of nuclear power for military ships was demonstrated in 1964 by the Navy's Operation Sea Orbit, in which three nuclear-powered surface ships, the carrier *Enterprise,* the frigate *Bainbridge* and the cruiser *Long Beach,* steamed more than 30,000 miles around the world without refueling. "For the first time in the history of the steam-powered ship," said Rear Admiral B. M. Strean, operational commander, "we broke the 'black oil tether' which binds combatant ships to their logistic support."

Two nonmilitary surface ships powered by atomic energy are already in use and others will soon join them. The U.S. Merchant Marine's N.S. *Savannah* has been in operation since 1962, and the Russian icebreaker *Lenin* since 1960. Soviet authorities were so pleased with the *Lenin* that they ordered construction of two additional nuclear-powered icebreakers. In Germany, the *Otto Hahn,* a nuclear-powered ore carrier, is scheduled for launching in 1967. Although the cost of nuclear power is still considerably above that of the oil-fired boiler, a number of marine experts argue that at least a dozen nuclear cargo ships could be operated profitably today over long-distance trade routes.

There are many naval architects, however, who feel that no conventional ship, regardless of how it is powered, will ever be able to go fast enough to meet all of the demands of the future. The speed of ocean-going ships has not increased at nearly the rate of land and air transportation. Since the beginnings of their commercial operation, rail, air and motor speeds have increased about 10-fold—trains from about 10 to about 100 miles per hour; passenger planes from 60 to 600; motorcars from about 12 to the 110-to-120 miles per hour that most commercial models are theoretically capable of today. Powered-ship speeds, by comparison, have increased less than threefold. The *Great Eastern*, in the 1860s, logged some 14 knots crossing the Atlantic. Today's fastest ocean liner, the *United States*, may average 32 knots.

The explanation for the lag in ship speed lies in simple hydrodynamics. The density of water is more than 800 times that of air, and therefore the frictional resistance encountered by a vessel is far greater than that experienced by a plane or land vehicle. Also, as William Froude discovered, a ship creates wave-making resistance, or drag, which increases geometrically with the speed of the ship. For this reason, when a conventional surface vessel reaches 40 knots it encounters a kind of speed barrier. To break it requires more power than the increased speed would justify economically. Moreover, higher speed would greatly magnify the vessel's response to waves; the intensified motions would imperil cargo and distress passengers and crew.

This speed limitation creates a serious gap in the spectrum of trans-oceanic services that are needed today and will be even more in demand in the future. What is lacking is a means of transportation about midway between the conventional ship and the air freighter, a carrier that combines some of the plane's speed with some of the ship's cargo space.

Boats that "fly"

Partial solutions may be provided by two new families of ships. Because these vessels avoid most frictional and wave-making resistance by "flying" a few feet above the water—one on subsurface wings, the other on a cushion of air—some ships of the future, operating on one or the other of these principles, may travel at 100 or more knots. Both kinds of craft are already in use on inland and coastal waters. The problem is one of adaptation: a great deal of testing and development remains to be done before it will be known whether ships of either type can be built large enough to serve as transoceanic vessels, or strong enough to meet the powerful

RIDING HIGH, the hulls of these boats are lifted off the water by three kinds of hydrofoils, structures which generate lift when water flows around them. Most early hydrofoil designs were ladder-shaped *(left);* as the boat gained speed, the foil-shaped rungs rose from the water. The surface-piercing foil *(center)* is a modification that uses a longer, angled foil to lift the boat higher as it moves faster. The fully submerged foil *(right)*, while not inherently as stable as the first two, is less affected by the action of waves.

SURFACE-PIERCING LADDER HYDROFOILS

SURFACE-PIERCING HYDROFOILS

FULLY SUBMERGED HYDROFOILS

forces of wind and waves on the open sea.

The hydrofoil craft, one of the two types now being considered for transoceanic use, was actually proposed as far back as 1869. The first known successful boat of the type was built by the Italian inventor Enrico Forlanini, and tested on Lake Maggiore in Switzerland in 1905. In the next few years, a number of other eminent inventors, including Alexander Graham Bell and the Wright brothers, experimented with the same strange water vehicle. In some of the early tests, speeds of more than 60 knots were achieved, but because of the lack of light-weight power plants, the boats were too heavy and too inefficient to be practical, and for many years interest languished. But there was renewed interest in the hydrofoil principle in Germany during World War II, and it has been growing stronger ever since.

Traveling on water stilts

The hydrofoil craft operates on much the same principle as the air-plane. Attached to the vessel by struts are sets of partially or totally submerged hydrofoils which have shaped surfaces that create lift just as the wings of an aircraft do.

The natural law which accounts for this phenomenon was discovered by Daniel Bernoulli, a Swiss mathematician, in 1738, in his study of fluids and gases in motion. According to Bernoulli's principle, the fast-er a fluid or gas is moving, the less pressure it exerts upon anything with which it comes into contact. If it flows faster along one side of an object than it does along the other, there will be a pressure differential. Thus, if water flows around a tear-shaped object, the pressure on the top and bottom sides will be the same because the two surfaces have the same configuration, and the water passes by them at the same rate. However, if the tear-shaped object is cut in half lengthwise so that the upper side remains curved but the lower is flat, the molecules of water going over the curved surface have a longer distance to travel and must move faster to keep up with the molecules flowing by the flat side: the pressure on the top side is now less than that below. Hydrofoils are built on this principle; the faster they move through the water, the great-er is the imbalance of pressures—and this imbalance forces the foils (and the hull attached to them) ever higher.

When a hydrofoil vessel is traveling at some 15 to 25 knots—depend-ing on its size—the foils lift the hull several feet above the surface of the water, thus practically eliminating both frictional and wave-making resistance. The speed of the craft is thereby increased dramatically. In tests, a hydrofoil has traveled 50 to 100 per cent faster than a conven-tional vessel of the same size and power.

There are two general types of foils now in use: "surface piercing" and "fully submerged." The surface-piercing variety is mounted on a U- or V-shaped frame attached to the hull, and in smooth water only part of the foil is submerged. Because the frames and foils extend some distance from the hull, they act as stabilizing fins in moderately rough

SUBCAVITATING FOIL

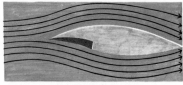

SUPERCAVITATING FOIL

CAVITATION is the phenomenon by which undesirable vapor bubbles *(light green)* form over a hydrofoil, reducing sustained lift and often damaging the foil. Cavitation occurs at about 60 knots. A partial solution to this problem is the sharp-edged supercavitating foil, which creates a large single cavity that breaks so far back that it does no harm. Supercavitating hydrofoil boats are expected to attain speeds over 100 knots.

water. For very rough seas, however, long, heavy, expensive struts are necessary; for this reason surface-piercing foils have thus far been employed largely on quiet lakes and rivers.

When fully submerged foils are used, the struts extend almost vertically downward from the hull. Because the foils remain completely immersed and have no inherent stability, they must be fitted with ailerons similar to those used on aircraft, to help them maintain a fixed depth. The ailerons are controlled by a highly sensitive, fast-acting autopilot that measures—mechanically or electronically—the height of oncoming waves and alters the lift of the foils accordingly.

The hydrofoil has already become a familiar sight skittering over European lakes and rivers, especially in the Soviet Union where land transportation is often inadequate. There are now several hundred of the craft in operation in Russian waters; the largest of them carries 300 passengers at some 40 knots. The hydrofoil has been less popular in the United States. On many U.S. waterways where it would be economically feasible to use the boats, the winds kick up a formidable chop. On waters where no wind problem exists, the service would have to buck stiff competition from well-established land transit systems.

Nevertheless, there are a number of the craft in commercial use in the United States—on the Potomac and Ohio Rivers, for example—and there are good prospects that additional lines will start operation in the near future. And the U.S. Navy has four hydrofoil vessels which are being tested on open waters. A fifth is under construction—the 212-foot *Plainview*, the world's largest hydrofoil craft, which is expected to travel at more than 70 knots on calm water, and twice as fast as conventional ships on rough seas.

The boiling-water problem

But serious problems still block the development of high-speed ocean-crossing hydrofoil ships. One of them is a phenomenon known as cavitation. When a foil is moving through the water at 50 to 60 knots, the pressure on its upper side becomes so low that the water boils, vapor-filled bubbles break off the trailing edge and lift is lost. Also, bubbles breaking against the foil cause erosion and the metal is quickly eaten away. To overcome the cavitation barrier, designers are experimenting with new "supercavitating" foils. One of the most promising has a wedge shape similar to that of an ax head instead of the conventional aircraft-wing profile. The cavity created by this form collapses well aft of the foil and thus has little effect on either lift or metal.

The stresses encountered by the foils at high speed provide another design problem. At 60 knots, foils must sustain dynamic pressures comparable to those an airplane wing endures at almost twice the speed of sound. Weight also poses enormous difficulties in the building of large hydrofoil ships. New materials are needed that are light enough for economical operation and yet are strong enough to meet the Merchant Marine's rigid safety requirements. In addition, much research and development remains to be done on autopilot controls and foil-retraction systems that would enable a big craft to move through comparatively shallow water.

However, the major obstacle to building large hydrofoil ships is something called the square-cube law. If the size of the foil is doubled, its lift is squared; i.e., it can lift four times as much. However, if the size of the ship is doubled, its weight is cubed; i.e., it becomes eight times as heavy. Also, a hydrofoil requires enormous power in relation to weight. The power plant needed to drive a 1,000-ton hydrofoil—about the size of a destroyer—at a speed of 60 knots would have to be capable of producing 120,000 horsepower, almost as much as is needed to drive the mighty 66,000-ton *France* at top speed.

Riding on an air cushion

Partly for these reasons, most experts have concluded that the new craft likely to cross the ocean in the near future will be a different sort of vessel entirely, probably the type known as an air-cushion vehicle. The ACV is a radical innovation that is less a boat than a strange kind of airplane that flies a few feet above the surface. It operates on a long-known principle: the resistance of air to compression. The craft maintains altitude, just a few feet above the surface, by means of fans that blow downward through the hull and establish a cushion of air between it and the water. As long as the volume of air in the cushion is kept constant by the fans, the craft will remain aloft at a stable height. The surface over which a vehicle of this type operates is immaterial; it skims over mud, bogs, swamps, ice and hard ground as easily as over water.

As in the case of the hydrofoil, the idea for the ACV is an old one. The concept was first proposed by Emanuel Swedenborg, a Swedish scientist and philosopher, in 1716, but it was not until 1935 that Toivo J. Kaario, a Finnish engineer, built and actually operated the first air-cushion vehicle. And it was only in the mid-1950s, when Christopher Cockerell, a British electronics engineer, designed the ACV he called the Hovercraft, that this innovation took off figuratively as well as literally.

Hovercraft Development Ltd. was formed in 1958, and a year later launched its first boat. Since then, two 15-passenger, seven-ton Hovercraft have begun ferrying passengers across San Francisco Bay. A few larger models with a capacity of 38 passengers each are operating in Scotland, Germany and Norway, and two others were scheduled to begin carrying passengers across the English Channel at 75 knots in 1966, reducing the ferry time from two and a half hours to about 30 minutes. There are plans to add a 500-passenger Hovercraft to the Channel fleet by 1968.

The United States Government is also interested in ACVs. The U.S. Navy's 65-foot *Hydroskimmer*, launched in 1963, has reached speeds of almost 70 knots in test runs, and a 100-ton ACV, the *Columbia*, designed to travel at speeds of 150 knots about seven feet above the water, has been proposed to the U.S. Maritime Administration.

But what happens when an ACV encounters waves considerably higher than its normal flying altitude (currently about six feet)? At present there are only two solutions, neither wholly satisfactory. The craft can settle on the water and ride out the rough weather like a conventional vessel, which means cutting back speed to a few knots, or it can remain aloft, following the contours of the surface—and giving a roller-coaster ride to those aboard.

Another problem confronting the ACV is leakage of air from the cushion that keeps the vessel aloft. There are two basic systems now in use to create the cushion. The first utilizes an "open plenum" chamber, something like an inverted bathtub with a hole at the top. A fan in the hole forces air straight downward into the center of the chamber, and the resistance of air to pressure lifts the craft. However, the air leaks out rapidly, resulting in a loss of pressure. A more widely used method involves an "annular jet." The fan-driven air, instead of going to the center of the chamber, is channeled to a ring of slots around the periphery of the hull. The slots are angled inward toward the center, and the force and direction of the air itself provide a seal which holds about 60 per cent of the cushion.

One important aid in maintenance of the air cushion came from a study of the test runs of the first Hovercraft. It was found that a flexible skirt, hung around the annular jets, was highly effective in reducing air leakage. Moreover, the skirt improved the performance of the craft in rough water. Because the skirt is flexible, small waves simply brush it aside in passing. When the waves are higher than the boat's altitude and longer than the hull, the skirt enables the ACV to follow the profile of the water. On another type of ACV, the same effect is achieved with thin, rigid skegs, or sidewalls, which project downward from the sides of the hull, plus flexible skirts beneath the bow and stern.

This ability to follow the contours of rough water has sharply reduced the anticipated need for power on projected oceangoing craft. At first, designers thought they would have to build ACVs capable of flying high enough to clear rough water, and this called for tremendous power (a craft hovering at six feet requires twice the power needed at three feet). "Profiling"—following the contour—did away with this necessity.

Lift and cargo space

Unlike the hydrofoil, the ACV benefits from increased size. There is a direct ratio between the dimensions of the hull and power needed to lift it: if the beam and length are doubled, the power must be doubled to maintain the same height. However, when those two dimensions of the hull are doubled, the load-carrying area is quadrupled. Therefore, the larger the craft, the more efficiently power is used.

Despite the problems still surrounding the designing and building of oceangoing ACVs, experts believe such craft will be in operation within the predictable future. A detailed analysis prepared for the Maritime Administration by one research company envisions a fleet of 5,000-

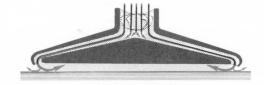

AN AIR-CUSHION VEHICLE literally rides on air above the water's surface. In the type shown here in schematic cross section, air is sucked through an intake and compressed. Then it is shunted down both sides of the ship and directed inward under the hull *(green arrows, above)* to create a "cushion" that lifts it off the water. The cushion is maintained by a continuous airflow that streams down and outward *(below)*.

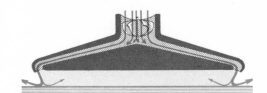

ton ACVs in the U.S. Merchant Marine by 1975. A ship of the proposed type would travel at 100 knots in comparatively smooth water, at 70 knots when waves are eight feet high, and at 40 to 50 knots in 30-foot waves. Computer studies of wave-height distribution indicate that the vessel could average 70 knots during 95 per cent of her time at sea. The craft would be fast enough to "fly" around most major storm centers, as an aircraft does; but if caught, the ACV would ride out the weather on the surface, like a conventional ship.

The ACV would deliver containerized cargo in lots of 1,000 to 1,500 tons several times a week instead of 10,000 tons once a month, as a conventional freighter does. Cargo would be carried at about five times the present speed, and the cost per ton-mile might be, in time, only slightly more.

Some experts are convinced that the realization of the fast transoceanic vessel is just over the horizon. How it will affect seaborne commerce is a matter of conjecture. "Our final goal is to replace ships," says one scientist, but no one seriously believes that. The world still needs mammoth tankers, containerized freighters, large, slow, low-cost bulk carriers. The day will never come when man can do without the ship, which over the centuries has carried him and his goods to every corner of the earth—and in the process has made civilization possible.

Exploring
the
Ocean Floor

"Knowledge of the oceans is more than a matter of curiosity. Our very survival may hinge upon it." When the late President Kennedy uttered these words in 1961, even the surface of the moon was more familiar to man than the land beneath the sea—a silent, sunless "inner space" three times greater in area than all the continents combined. Since Kennedy spoke, men have been invading the depths on an ever-growing scale: Jacques-Yves Cousteau and his "Oceanauts" have lived for weeks at a time in an underwater community in the Red Sea, making sallies to 1,000 feet. Swarms of odd little vessels are carrying scientists, prospectors and sightseers along the floor of the continental shelves. And to plumb the real depths, scientists are building blimplike bathyscaphes that have already probed to the floor of the Pacific Ocean's Marianas Trench—an abyss seven miles deep where the water pressure is almost seven tons per square inch.

CONQUEROR OF THE ABYSS
As metal ballast pellets are discharged from its belly, the bathyscaphe *Trieste*, designed by Swiss inventor Auguste Piccard, is inspected by divers. It was the first vessel to dive 35,500 feet to the Pacific floor. The crew rides in the spherical gondola; the huge, sausage-shaped skin above it contains gasoline which, being lighter than water, lifts the *Trieste* to the surface when ballast is released.

A School
of Baby Subs

The tiny submarines shown here are some of the miniature vessels that are beginning to invade the waters of the continental shelf. Some are sturdy enough to reach a depth of 600 feet where they may be used for serious work like scientific research, salvage and prospecting. Already, with their help, the sea floor is being mined for tin, oil and diamonds. The subs' small size makes them ideal for this work; they are subjected to less total compression than conventional submarines at the same depths, so

their hulls can be thinner, lighter and more maneuverable.

There is also a small fleet of pleasure subs. Most of these are so-called "wet" subs—that is, they are flooded to neutralize the pressure on their hulls, and are manned by crews who wear normal diving gear. They can go only as deep as the divers can, but they provide motive power and can carry tools and instruments. In such craft sportsmen will someday cruise along the ocean floor as comfortably as though they were on dry land.

SEARCHING FOR THE PAST

The *Asherah,* here being lifted from the water, is named after the Phoenician goddess of the sea, and has been used by archeologists searching for relics on the floor of the Aegean. Two battery-driven propellers drive and steer this custom-built, $100,000 sub which carries a two-man crew to a depth of 600 feet. Its top speed under water is about five miles per hour.

AN UNDERWATER CONVENTION

Nine different kinds of miniature undersea craft and tows converge on a salvage balloon (used for lifting objects to the surface) at Florida's Silver Springs. The vessel nearest the marker at left center is a pleasure craft—the rest were designed primarily for research and exploration.

A BUG-EYED WATER BABY

The Perry *Cubmarine* carries a two-man crew to a depth of 225 feet, where it cruises at speeds up to nine miles per hour over a range of about 40 miles. Vertical motion is controlled by diving planes and by a ballast system. Oxygen for the crew is carried in pressurized bottles.

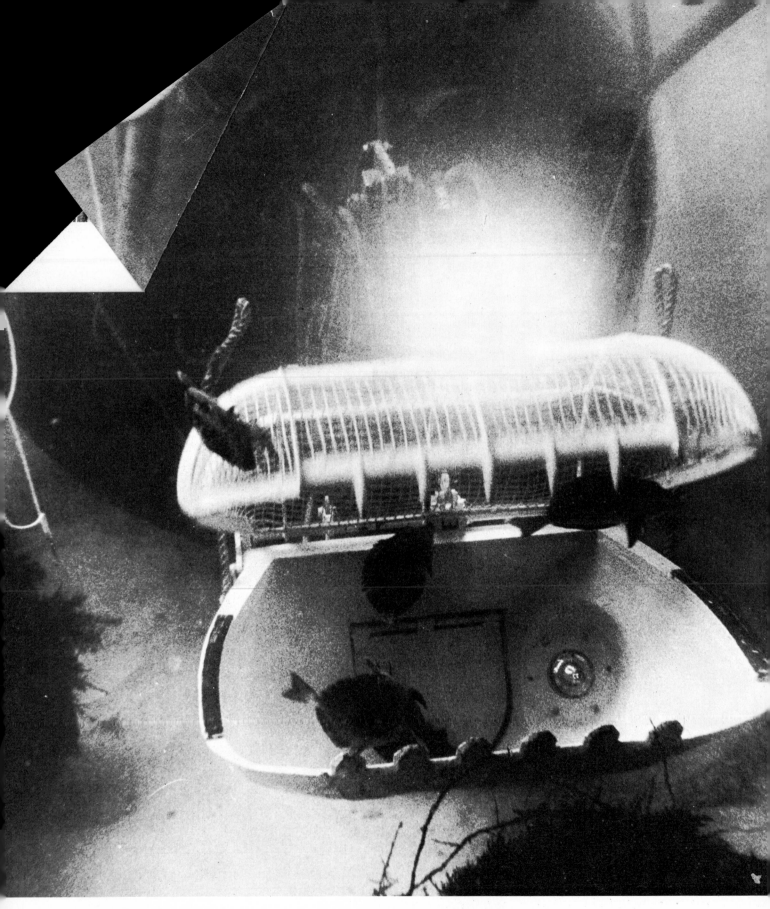

THE CATCHER IN THE DEEP

Collecting fishes for scientific study, the *Yomi-urigo*'s fish-catcher gathers in specimens that are attracted by a bright light projecting from the bow. The catcher is connected by a tunnel-like tube to a pressurized tank in the vessel. In this tank marine specimens can be transported from deep water to the surface without being subjected to drastic reduction in water pressure.

A Japanese Sub-of-All-Trades

Japan's reasons for exploring the sea are probably more pressing than any other country's. Its population subsists to a large extent on fish, its mineral resources on land are fast dwindling, and its cities are periodically shattered by earthquakes that originate beneath the sea. Spurred by these incentives, Japan is building a small fleet of oceanographic research submarines.

The first of these, the *Yomiurigo*, launched in 1964, sports more ingenious attachments than a de luxe vacuum cleaner. Besides such standard items as television and sonar, it has a "magic hand" for gathering rocks and plants, a mud collector, a plankton trap and various devices that measure such deep-sea secrets as underwater thermal streams and gravitational and magnetic forces. Some of its most practical work is done with the gaping fish-catcher shown at left.

Yomiurigo is unloaded from its mother ship, which totes it to and from dives to save power.

A MAN-MADE SEA MONSTER
Like a curious sea turtle, the *Yomiurigo* gropes for specimens on the ocean floor with its fish-catcher *(also seen at left)*. The vessel carries its six-man crew to a maximum depth of about 1,000 feet, where it can cruise for six hours at two miles per hour. The Japanese are also developing three-man oceanographic subs that can explore at a depth of about 2,000 feet.

183

A Vessel for Men Who Live in the Sea

Perhaps the pre-eminent figure in underwater exploration is Frenchman Jacques-Yves Cousteau, whose celebrated *Diving Saucer* has done more practical underwater research than any other craft. Cousteau, who also designed the portable breathing gear that has revolutionized underwater exploration, has sent the *Diving Saucer* on more than 100 dives to 1,000 feet, and in the process has gathered a wealth of scientific information.

The *Saucer* is also the spearhead of Operation Conshelf, Cousteau's daring scheme "not only to explore but to inhabit the sea." On the floor of the Red Sea, off the coast of Sudan, Cousteau and his Oceanauts have built a cluster of steel shells which are filled with air, like cups turned upside down and lowered into a tub. Here men live and work under pressure with the same nonchalance that other men display on dry land—though they encounter some very peculiar phenomena. For example, the helium substituted for nitrogen in the air to prevent painful attacks of the bends causes the most masculine voice to come out in a ludicrous, high-pitched squawk—a phenomenon known as the "Donald Duck effect."

THE SAUCER AND ITS CREATOR
Wearing an aqualung, his most famous invention, Jacques-Yves Cousteau films his *Diving Saucer*. The *Saucer*, made mostly of three-quarter-inch steel, is driven by water jets from two rotating nozzles, one of which is visible here. Cousteau has also designed another vessel called the *Deepstar*, which resembles the *Saucer* but is built to dive as deep as 4,000 feet.

NO ROOM TO SPARE

Wedged into the *Diving Saucer* like sardines, Oceanauts peer through the portholes. Between them is the ballast tank, which is filled with water to make the *Saucer* sink, and is blown out to make it buoyant again. An instrument panel, with depth gauges, sonar and other devices, rings the interior. The picture was taken with a 180°-lens camera at the top of the cabin.

A HAND BENEATH THE SEA

Alvin's mechanical hand, manipulated from inside the pressure hull, snatches a seashell and holds it up for inspection. The one-and-a-third-inch-thick steel spherical pressure hull is 6 feet 10 inches in diameter. But the rest of *Alvin*'s hull, which is flooded during dives and therefore does not have to be pressure-resistant, is covered by a skin only an eighth-inch thick.

The *Alvin,* here making a test dive, is named after Dr. Allyn Vine of the Woods Hole Oceanographic Institution, whose scientists operate the vessel.

A Vehicle for Greater Depths

Water pressure is not the only obstacle to deep diving: William Beebe was lowered by cable to 3,028 feet in his bathysphere in 1934. But it complicates the problem of ascent and descent. The object is to make the deep-sea craft just buoyant enough so it can sink, rise or hover at will. The research vessel *Alvin,* seen here, operates at 6,000 feet, where water pressure is almost 2,780 pounds per square inch. *Alvin* gets neutral buoyancy, or "hoverability," from air-filled spheres and pressure-proof plastic foam. Vertical movements are controlled by an ingenious flotation system *(below)* that eliminates the need for metal ballast.

HOW "ALVIN" GOES UP AND DOWN

Before submerging *(top drawing, right),* *Alvin's* main ballast tank is flooded with water *(blue);* then oil is pumped into the rigid reservoirs from the rubber flotation bags, which collapse and decrease in volume. *Alvin's* total weight is unchanged, but with less volume it displaces less water and therefore sinks. Unlike other deep-sea craft, *Alvin* does not have to release tons of metal ballast to ascend: its flotation bags are simply pumped full of oil again. Trim is maintained by pumping mercury and oil back and forth between fore and aft tanks as needed.

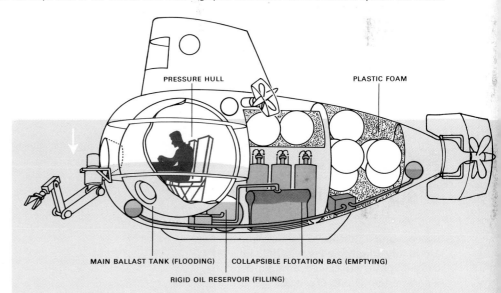

PRESSURE HULL

PLASTIC FOAM

MAIN BALLAST TANK (FLOODING)

COLLAPSIBLE FLOTATION BAG (EMPTYING)

RIGID OIL RESERVOIR (FILLING)

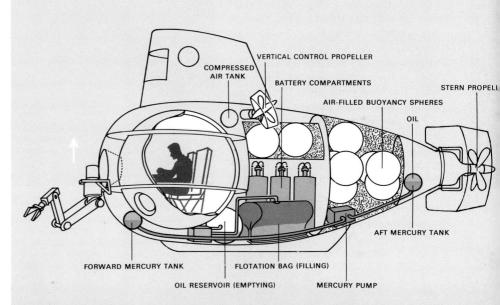

COMPRESSED AIR TANK

VERTICAL CONTROL PROPELLER

BATTERY COMPARTMENTS

AIR-FILLED BUOYANCY SPHERES

STERN PROPELL

OIL

AFT MERCURY TANK

FORWARD MERCURY TANK

FLOTATION BAG (FILLING)

OIL RESERVOIR (EMPTYING)

MERCURY PUMP

The *Aluminaut* surfaces, blowing water from its ballast tanks to gain enough freeboard for surface cruising. It is strictly a research vessel,

Breaking the Weight Barrier

Conventional military submarines are highly adaptable vessels, but they cannot venture to the ocean's depths. The problem is one of weight: a full-sized self-buoyant steel hull thick enough to withstand titanic deep-sea pressures would be so heavy that it would sink like a brick. On the other hand, the bulky external buoyancy systems that support the pressure hulls of craft like the *Trieste* make them highly unmaneuverable.

One attempt to combine maneuverability with deep-sea capability is the *Aluminaut*, an experimental aluminum-hulled submarine light enough to float unassisted and strong enough to dive to 15,000 feet—more than 10 times deeper than any conventional sub. If the *Aluminaut* succeeds, it will bring nearly 62 per cent of the ocean floor in range of easy exploration.

PUTTING THE LID ON A DIVE

A diver adjusts a cover over the *Aluminaut*'s ballast tube while the craft is at the surface. The cover is removed before a dive, and the ballast is held in place by powerful electromagnets.

The 53-foot *Aluminaut* is manned by a crew of three and contains modest but adequate living facilities: a food locker, a coffee maker, a few gallons of fresh water and a chemical toilet.

despite its superficial resemblance to military submarines. The horizontal propeller on its deck is used while performing vertical maneuvers.

BALLAST FOR A THREE-MILE DIVE

The *Aluminaut* carries three kinds of ballast to aid it in diving and ascending. At the start of a dive *(top diagram)*, the water-ballast tanks are flooded. For the ascent *(bottom)*, metal ballast pellets are released; in an emergency the heavy ballast bar can be dropped. If power fails, the dead electromagnets drop all metal ballast. The craft's aluminum hull, though six and a half inches thick, still weighs only 107,000 pounds, one third the weight of a steel hull the same size and strength. Its light weight combined with large volume provide the needed buoyancy.

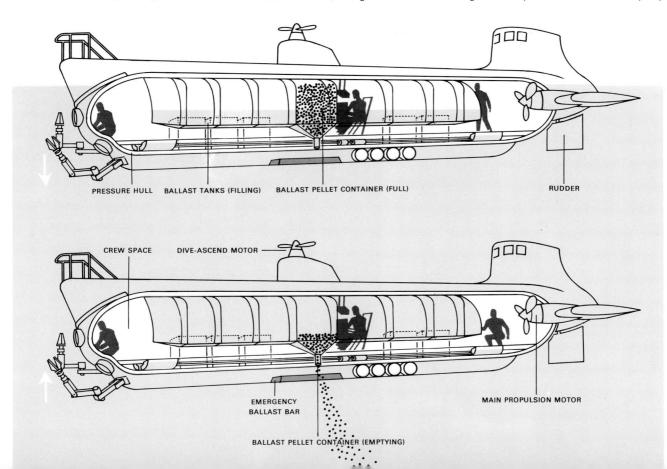

PRESSURE HULL   BALLAST TANKS (FILLING)   BALLAST PELLET CONTAINER (FULL)   RUDDER

CREW SPACE   DIVE-ASCEND MOTOR

EMERGENCY BALLAST BAR   MAIN PROPULSION MOTOR

BALLAST PELLET CONTAINER (EMPTYING)

Designed for Seven Miles Down

The French bathyscaphe *Archimède*, named for the Greek thinker who discovered the principle of buoyancy, is more balloon than submarine. (Auguste Piccard, originator of bathyscaphes, was also a brilliant innovator in aerial balloon design.) But instead of being supported by helium, it is buoyed by gasoline: some 5,200 cubic feet of it, in a thin steel shell. Like the *Trieste*, it is designed for the deepest dives of all, seven miles down.

Bathyscaphes are clumsy and very limited both in working space and range of movement on the bottom. Someday they may be replaced by roomier, more maneuverable craft. But they have taken man as deep as he can go, and for years will go on doing invaluable service as explorers on the frontiers of "inner space."

MASTER OF THE DEEP

With its ballast tanks empty and its "balloon" full of gasoline, *Archimède* floats. But it sinks when water floods its ballast tanks *(top)*. There are also holes in the bottom of the gasoline-filled hull, so that water can enter to equalize pressures as the craft descends. To ascend, the occupants drop metal pellets. The crew enters and leaves the pressure sphere through the forward ballast tank after it has been drained.

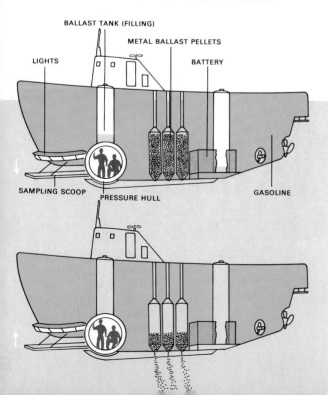

A Glossary of Sea Terms

AFT At, near or toward the stern of a vessel.

AMIDSHIPS On the longitudinal center line of the ship; or the waist or middle part of the ship midway between bow and stern.

BALLAST Weight put in the lower parts of a vessel for stability. Usually metal, or water or oil carried in tanks.

BARK A three- or four-masted sailing ship, square-rigged on the forward masts and fore-and-aft rigged on the aftermost mast.

BEAM The greatest breadth of a vessel. Also, one of the timbers or steel members stretching across a ship on which the decks are laid.

BOW The forward part of a vessel.

BRIDGE The elevated platform from which the vessel is navigated; usually amidships, but far aft on many cargo vessels.

BRIG A two-masted sailing ship, square-rigged on both masts. Also, a ship's jail.

BRIGANTINE A two-masted sailing ship, square-rigged on the forward mast, fore-and-aft rigged on the mainmast.

BUOY A floating navigational aid, anchored to the bottom, which marks hazards such as rocks or shoals, or indicates the boundaries of channels.

BUOYANCY The tendency of a body to float when immersed in water. The center of buoyancy is the point in a ship where the sum of all upward forces is assumed to act.

CHRONOMETER An accurate seagoing timepiece, set to Greenwich time, which is essential for celestial navigation.

DRAFT The depth of a vessel from keel to water line.

FATHOM A unit of length measuring six feet, the common measure of water depth in the United States and Britain.

FORE Referring to the forward part of a vessel.

FORE-AND-AFT Along the longitudinal axis of a ship; a manner of rigging sailing ships so that the sails are set roughly parallel with the keel instead of across the vessel.

FORECASTLE A raised forward deck in merchant steamers; also a forward living compartment for the crew. Often written and pronounced "fo'c'sle." Originally a turreted structure affording vantage for a ship's fighting men.

FULL-RIGGED SHIP A sailing ship of three or more masts rigged with square sails on all masts.

FUNNEL The smokestack of a steam or motor vessel.

GREENWICH TIME The local time at the Greenwich Royal Observatory in England, by which all navigational calculations are reckoned. Established as the standard time by international convention in 1884.

HYDROFOIL A structure shaped so that water flowing around it will create lift, as an airplane wing provides lift. When attached to a ship's hull, hydrofoils raise the moving hull from the water and permit a smoother, faster ride. Also, any boat equipped with hydrofoils.

KEEL The backbone of a ship, from which the ribs project. Also, the underwater structure of a sailboat that provides stability and resistance to lateral movement.

KNOT A unit measure of speed equal to one nautical mile per hour; often incorrectly used as "knots per hour." The word derives from an early method of telling a vessel's speed by counting the knots in a line as it unreeled from the stern of a moving vessel.

LATITUDE The distance north or south of the equator, measured in degrees, from 0° at the equator to 90° at the poles.

LONGITUDE The distance east or west of the prime, or Greenwich, meridian, which is a circle drawn around the earth through the poles and through the site of the Greenwich Royal Observatory in England. Longitude is measured in degrees from 0° (at Greenwich) to 180° (the opposite side of the globe).

NAUTICAL MILE The length of a minute, or one sixtieth of a degree, of latitude, used in measuring all nautical distances. It is measured at 6,080 feet, 800 feet more than a statute mile; but for short distances it is standardized at 2,000 yards.

POOP The deck area aft of the aftermost mast in a square rigger; also, a raised deck aft on a modern vessel.

PORT (A) The left side of a vessel, looking forward. (B) A harbor for taking on or discharging passengers or cargo. (C) An opening in the side of a ship, as for ventilation or guns.

SCHOONER A fore-and-aft rigged sailing ship of three or more masts of equal height, or of two masts where the forward mast is the shorter.

SEXTANT An instrument for measuring angles, used primarily in celestial navigation for determining the position of heavenly bodies in relation to the horizon.

STARBOARD The right side of a vessel, looking forward.

STEM The forwardmost upright structural member of a ship's hull.

STERN The after part of the vessel.

SUPERSTRUCTURE The parts of the ship above the highest full deck.

TACKING The zigzag progress made by a sailboat heading for a destination upwind. The procedure involves sailing as close as possible to the wind, first on one side and then on the other.

TOPSIDES The area of the ship's skin between the water line and the rail.

6,000 Years on the Seas

In his long struggle to master the sea, man has launched an enormous variety of ships of every size, shape and function. The 48 surface vessels shown here include representatives of significant types as well as some of history's most famous vessels. Each ship is identified by name or by type, the date or period it was built and its length (in some cases estimated).

For at least 50 centuries of marine history, ships were made of wood and were driven by sails or oars. But within 100 years after the successful introduction of steam power in 1807, almost all shipping had converted to steam and steel. Whether in wood or steel, a ship's design has always reflected its special purpose. The 18th Century *Victory*, for example, was a powerful floating fortress, while the clean lines of the brigantine of the same period bespoke her role as a swift cargo carrier. This specialization has been carried to an extreme in such modern ships as the *Enterprise*, with its severe "flattop" profile, and the long, low *Nissho Maru*, which could carry enough oil to float the *Victory*, with plenty more to spare.

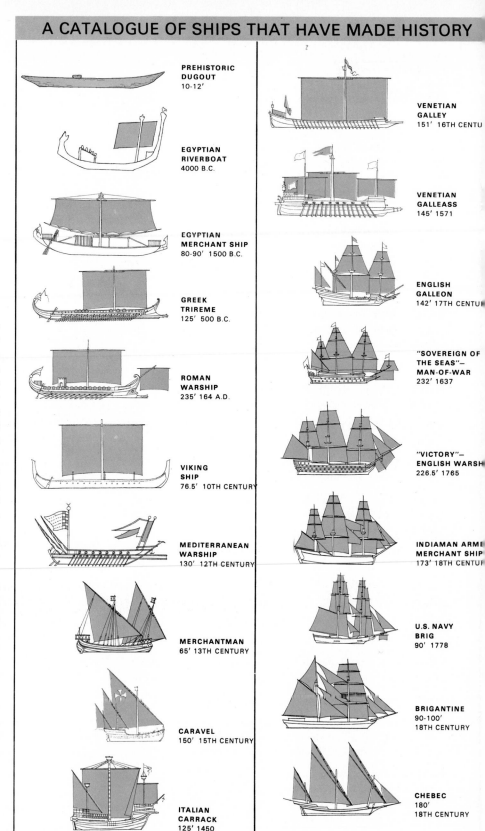

PREHISTORIC DUGOUT
10-12'

EGYPTIAN RIVERBOAT
4000 B.C.

EGYPTIAN MERCHANT SHIP
80-90' 1500 B.C.

GREEK TRIREME
125' 500 B.C.

ROMAN WARSHIP
235' 164 A.D.

VIKING SHIP
76.5' 10TH CENTURY

MEDITERRANEAN WARSHIP
130' 12TH CENTURY

MERCHANTMAN
65' 13TH CENTURY

CARAVEL
150' 15TH CENTURY

ITALIAN CARRACK
125' 1450

VENETIAN GALLEY
151.5' 16TH CENTU

VENETIAN GALLEASS
145' 1571

ENGLISH GALLEON
142' 17TH CENTU

"SOVEREIGN OF THE SEAS"— MAN-OF-WAR
232' 1637

"VICTORY"— ENGLISH WARSH
226.5' 1765

INDIAMAN ARME MERCHANT SHIP
173' 18TH CENTU

U.S. NAVY BRIG
90' 1778

BRIGANTINE
90-100' 18TH CENTURY

CHEBEC
180' 18TH CENTURY

THE EARLIEST VESSELS, starting with the primitive dugout and continuing through antiquity, were propelled by oars or a single, square sail. During the Middle Ages, triangular lateen sails were introduced, and later were incorporated in the two- or three-masted carrack.

THE AGE OF SAIL lasted through the 16th, 17th and 18th Centuries. In response to the competitive demands of warfare, trade and global exploration, large wooden-hulled, full-rigged warships and merchant vessels were built that could sail anywhere in the world.

"CONSTITUTION"—
AMERICAN
WARSHIP
204' 1797

BARK
335'
19TH CENTURY

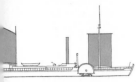

"CLERMONT"—
STEAMBOAT
140' 1807

BALTIMORE
CLIPPER
112' 1845

WHALING
SHIP
107'
19TH CENTURY

"FLYING CLOUD"—
CALIFORNIA
CLIPPER
209.5' 1851

KETCH
84' 19TH CENTURY

"GREAT
EASTERN"—
STEAMSHIP
692' 1858

"GLOIRE"—
STEAMSHIP
252.5' 1859

CHINESE
JUNK
100'
19TH CENTURY

JAPANESE
JUNK
80'
19TH CENTURY

"MONITOR"—IRONCLAD WARSHIP 172' 1862

"NATCHEZ"—MISSISSIPPI STEAMBOAT 307' 1869

"DREADNOUGHT"—EARLY BATTLESHIP 526' 1906

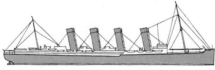

"MAURETANIA"—LINER 790' 1906

"WYOMING"—
SCHOONER
350' 1910

"SELANDIA"—CARGO VESSEL 370' 1911

"SAN FRANCISCO"—HEAVY CRUISER 588' 1934

LIBERTY SHIP CARGO VESSEL 418' 1942

"O'BANNON"—DESTROYER 376.5' 1942

LANDING SHIP 453' 1942

"MISSOURI"—BATTLESHIP 800' 1944

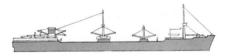

WHALE FACTORY 639' 1950

"UNITED STATES"—LINER 990' 1952

"LENIN"—ICEBREAKER 440' 1957

"ENTERPRISE"—AIRCRAFT CARRIER 1,102' 1961

"NISSHO MARU"—CARGO SHIP 954.71' 1962

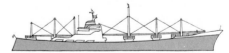

"CHALLENGER"—CARGO LINER 544' 1964

"HAWAIIAN MONARCH"—CONTAINER-SHIP 630.5' 1965

END OF AN ERA, the period from the close of the 18th Century to the mid-19th Century saw the wooden sailing vessel reach its zenith in the swift clipper ship; but the successful trials of the *Clermont* foreshadowed a new age of steam power that put an end to the days of sail.

A TIME OF TRANSITION from wood and sail to iron and steam occurred in the middle 19th Century. While primitive junks still sailed in the East, and large six-masted schooners later appeared in American coastal waters, most ships by 1900 were metal-hulled and steam-driven.

PRESENT-DAY SHIPS are chiefly made of steel and powered by steam, diesel or nuclear machinery. Though faster, more specialized and technically superior to their predecessors, their functions are still fundamentally the same—as cargo carriers, passenger liners or ships of war.

195

FURTHER READING

General

Bassett-Lowke, W. J., and George Holland, *Ships and Men*. George G. Harrap, 1946.

Casson, Lionel, *The Ancient Mariners*. Macmillan, 1959.

Gilfillan, S. C., *Inventing the Ship*. Follett, 1935.

Landström, Björn, *The Ship*. Doubleday, 1961.

McDowell, William, *The Shape of Ships*. Hutchison, 1950.

McEwen, W. A., and A. H. Lewis, *Encyclopedia of Nautical Knowledge*. Cornell Maritime Press, 1953.

Singer, Charles, and others, eds., *A History of Technology* (5 vols.). Oxford University Press, 1954-1958.

Society of Naval Architects & Marine Engineers, *Historical Transactions, 1893-1943*. SNAME, 1945.

Sailing Ships

Anderson, Romola, and R. C., *The Sailing-Ship*. W. W. Norton, 1963.

†Bathe, B. W., *Ship Models* (Parts I, II and III). Her Majesty's Stationery Office, 1963.

Chapelle, Howard I., *The History of American Sailing Ships*. W. W. Norton, 1935.

†Clowes, G.S. Laird, *Sailing Ships* (Part I). Her Majesty's Stationery Office, 1962.

Morison, Samuel Eliot, *Admiral of the Ocean Sea*. Little, Brown, 1942.

Rosenfeld, Morris and Stanley, and William H. Taylor, *The Story of American Yachting*. Appleton-Century-Crofts, 1958.

Powered Ships

Angas, W. Mack, *Rivalry on the Atlantic*. Lee Furman, 1939.

Dugan, James, *The Great Iron Ship*. Harper & Row, 1953.

LaDage, John H., et al., *Merchant Ships*. Cornell Maritime Press, 1955.

Morrison, John H., *History of American Steam Navigation*. Stephen Daye Press, 1958.

Warships

Baar, James, and William C. Howard, *Polaris!* Harcourt, Brace, 1960.

Polmar, Norman, *Atomic Submarines*. D. Van Nostrand, 1963.

Potter, E. B., and Chester Nimitz, eds., *Sea Power*. Prentice-Hall, 1960.

Robinson, S. S., and Mary, *A History of Naval Tactics*. U.S. Naval Institute, 1942.

Rush, C. W., W. C. Chambliss and H. J. Gimpel, *The Complete Book of Submarines*. World Publishing Company, 1963.

Design and Building of Ships

Abell, Sir Westcott, *The Shipwright's Trade*. Caravan Book Service, 1962.

Baker, Elijah III, *Introduction to Steel Shipbuilding*. McGraw-Hill, 1953.

Baker, G. S., *The Merchant Ship*. Sigma Books, 1948.

LaDage, John H., *Modern Ships* (2nd ed.). Cornell Maritime Press, 1965.

Tryckare, Tre, *The Lore of Ships*. Holt, Rinehart & Winston, 1963.

Navigation

Bowditch, Nathaniel, *American Practical Navigator*. U.S. Government Printing Office, 1962.

Collinder, Per, *A History of Marine Navigation*. B. T. Batsford, 1954.

Lane, Carl D., and John Montgomery, *Navigation the Easy Way*. W. W. Norton, 1949.

Mixter, George W., *Primer of Navigation* (4th ed.). D. Van Nostrand, 1960.

Taylor, E.G.R., and N. W. Richey, *The Geometrical Seaman*. St. Martin's Press, 1963.

Underwater Research Vehicles

Dugan, James, and Richard Vahan, eds., *Men under Water*. Chilton Books, 1965.

Park, Frank, "Deep-sea Vehicles." *International Science and Technology*, March, 1965.

Piccard, Jacques, and R. S. Dietz, *Seven Miles Down*. G. P. Putnam's Sons, 1961.

Terry, R. D., *The Case for the Deep Submersible*. Western Periodicals, 1966.

†Available only in paperback edition.

ACKNOWLEDGMENTS

The editors of this book are indebted to the following persons and institutions: Vice Admiral Constantine Alexandris, Royal Hellenic Navy, Director of the Naval Museum, Piraeus; Mrs. Theda Bassett and Lt. Donald J. Kazimir, U.S. Naval Submarine Base, Groton, Conn.; B. W. Bathe, Science Museum, London; Ragnvald Bernt, Ross, Calif.; Maria Luisa Bonelli, Museum of the History of Science, Florence, Italy; Frank Braynard, Moran Towing and Transportation Co., New York City; Dr. John P. Breslin, Director, and Daniel Savitsky, Davidson Laboratory, Stevens Institute of Technology; Robert H. Burgess, The Mariners Museum, Newport News, Va.; Lionel Casson, Professor of Classics, New York University; Baron Gianbattista Rubin de Cervino and Gennaro Mottola, Museum of Naval History, Venice, Italy; Lt. G. C. Clark, Lt. Commander Philip Danahy, Lt. Commander David Linde and Lt. J. Goldthorpe, U.S. Coast Guard; Colonel Athanasios Deligiorgis, Royal Hellenic Air Force; Dr. Robert F. Dill, U.S. Navy Electronics Laboratory, San Diego; Admiral Filippo Ferrari-Aggradi and Captain Nereo Benussi, Italian Naval Command, Venice; Dr. Paul Fye, Director, Woods Hole Oceanographic Institute, Woods Hole, Mass.; Norman H. Gaber, Battelle Memorial Institute, Columbus; J.R.R. Harter and L.C. Morris, Reynold Submarine Services Corp., Miami; Ralston Hayden, American Bureau of Shipping, New York City; James A. Higgins, Office of Research and Development, Morton Simmons, Intelligence Office, and Jack Tennant, Public Relations Officer, Maritime Administration; Capt. William Hurder,

U.S. Merchant Marine Academy, Kings Point, N.Y.; Lt. Commander Demosthenes Ioannidis and Commander George Soubasakos, Royal Hellenic Navy; Rudolf F. Lehnert, Department of Aerospace and Mechanical Sciences, Princeton University; P. R. Loughman, General Dynamics, Groton, Conn.; Giovanni Mariacher, Correr Museum, Venice, Italy; Ray Meinhardt, Litton Industries, Minneapolis; Stuart Miller, Westland S. A., Washington, D.C.; Duke Enrico Montalto, Sovereign Military Order of Malta, Rome; George Naish, National Maritime Museum, London; Michael Papaconstantinou, Deputy, Greek Parliament; Harold L. Peterson, National Park Service, Washington, D.C.; Dimitri Rebikoff, Rebikoff Oceanics, Chicago; Lt. William F. Rope, Naval History Division and Jane T. Wootton and Harvey F. Chaplin Jr., David Taylor Model Basin, Department of the Navy.

The editors appreciate the assistance of the officers and crew of the S.S. *France*, especially: Captain Joseph Ropars; Chief Pursers Roger Joubert and Pierre Boilève; Purser Jean-Paul Giquel; Chief Engineer Pierre Leguillon and Assistant Chief Engineer Raymond Guillemette; Assistant Chief Electrician Louis Pelgé; the Officers of the Deck; Mlle. Jacqueline Métifeu; and Peter J. Rossi, French Line Publicity Department. For the picture essay on shipbuilding, the editors appreciate the assistance of Nils Svensson, Managing Director, A. B. Götaverken, Göteborg, Sweden; and the following members of his staff: Carl Eric Boström, Director of Public Relations; Erik Setteskog and Lars Sjögren.

INDEX

Numerals in italics indicate a photograph or painting of the subject mentioned.

Gasoline engine, in submarines, 128-129
Gato-class submarine, *132*
Geographic (true) north, 155, *162*
George Washington, U.S.S., 133-134; model tests of, *48-49*
German Navy, *146-147*, 148; U-boats, 129, 130-131, 148
Gloire, S.S., *195*
Glückauf, tanker, 83
GM, measure of stability, 12
Gokstad ship, 56, 57, *194*
Gong buoy, *160*
Gorch Fock, square-rigger, *52*
Göteborg, Arendal shipyard, 16, *17-29*
Grace, W. R., and Company, 106
Gravity: center of, 11, *12-13;* force of, 11, *12-13*, *124*
Great Britain, S.S., 78, 80
Great Eastern, S.S., 31, 32, 78-79, 173, *195*
Great Western, S.S., 77
Greeks: geographical knowledge of, *map* 153; navigation of, 151, 154; sailing vessels, 55; at Salamis, 136, *137;* triremes, *136-137*, *194*
Greenwich (England) time, 156, 164
Greyhound, vessel, 34
Gross tonnage, *diagram* 14
Guadalcanal, U.S.S., *115*
Gunn, Ross, 131
Guns, on warships, *142-145*, 147; introduction of, 59, 134, 138, *139-141;* introduction of explosive shells, 134, 144; revolving turret, 134, *144*
"Guppy"-type submarine, *132*
Gyassa, Egyptian, 53, *55*

H

Hanno the Carthaginian, 54
Harbor facilities. *See* Port facilities
Harbor fees, basis of, 15
Harrison, John, 157
Hawaiian Monarch, S.S., *195*
Hawkins, John, 140
Heated tankers, 105, 106
Heave, 37, *diagram* 39
Heeling, 11, *12-13*, 44. *See also* Roll
Henry VIII, King of England, 32
Henry the Navigator, Prince, 155
Hero of Alexandria, 81
Herodotus, 151
High-pressure boilers, 78, 81
Hipparchus, 154
Hitler, Adolf, 131
H. L. Hunley, submarine, 126-*127*
Hodgson, James, 78
Holland, John P., 128
Holland, U.S.S., 128
Horse boats, *76*
Housatonic, U.S.S., 127
Hovercraft, 176, *177*
Hugo, Victor, 58
Hull: marks on, *10-11*, 14; need for flexibility of, 13; rust-proofing of, *20;* surface coating of, and frictional resistance, 33
Hull construction: carvel *vs.* clinker-built, 54, *58*, *59;* materials, 10, 13, 31, 54, 75, 77-79, 87, 194, 195; modern, 13, 15, *17*, 19, *20-27;* Roman merchantman, 54
Hull design, 31, 37; antipitching devices, 40, 46; antirolling devices, 38, 46, 87, *88-89;* of clipper, 60, *61;* fishlike, *33;* of full-rigged ship, 58, *59;* of galleon, *33;* of icebreakers, *120;* length, 39, 46; model-testing, 10, 32-34, 39-40, *41-45*, *50-51;* of modern ocean liner, 96; of northern cog, 57, 58, *59;* of Roman merchantman and southern ship, 54, *58;* of racing yacht, *50-51;* of submarines, 124, *132*-133; of Viking longship, 56, *59;* and wave spectrum analysis, 37, 39; of wooden ships, 13. *See also* Length-to-beam ratio
Hull fins, stabilizing, 38, 46, 87, *88-89*
Hulls, Jonathan, 76
Hunley, Horace L., 126, 127
Hydraulic press, *24-25*
Hydraulic steering mechanism, 88, *92-93*
Hydrofoil: principle of operation, 174; types of, *173*, *174*, 175
Hydrofoil craft, 110, *112-113*, *173*, 174-176
Hydrogen peroxide, as submarine fuel, 130-131
Hydroskimmer, ACV, 176

I

Icebreakers, 110, *120-121*, 172, *195*
Imports, U.S. waterborne, 103
Indiaman armed merchant ship, *194*
Inertial navigation, 124
Instruments, navigational, *92*, 93, *159*, *162*, *164*, *166;* automation, 172; early, 57, 151, 154-157; modern, 157-158, *164*, *166*
Iron construction, 10, 13, 31, 77-79, 134, 195
Iron Duke, H.M.S., *147*
Ironclads, *144-145*, *195*

J

Japanese junk, *195*
Jet propulsion, early attempts at, 76
Jib, 59, *diagram* 65, *70*
Jibboom, 59
Jouffroy d'Abbans, Marquis Claude de, 76
Junk, *68-69;* Chinese, 53, 56, 62, *195;* Japanese, *195*
Jutland, Battle of, *146-147*

K

Kaario, Toivo J., 176
Keel, 13
Kennedy, John F., 178
Ketch, *195*
Kirk, A.C., 81
Kistiakowsky, George, 131
Knots, origin of term, 157

L

Lafayette-class submarine, *132*
Lakatoi, New Guinean, 53, *54*
Lake, Simon, 128-129
Landing ship, *195*
Larboard (ladeborde), 56
Lardner, Dionysius, 77
Lateen rig, *55*-56, *58*, *59*, *69*, *194*
Lateener, 56, 57, *58*, 62
Latitude, 153; determination by celestial readings, 153-155
Launching methods, *8*, 15, 18-19
Lead-and-line depth sounding, 57, 151, 166
Least-time track, 37
Lee, Ezra, 126
Length of ships, and pitch, 39, 44
Length-to-beam ratios: conventional submarine, 132; general, of modern ships, 120; of icebreakers, 120; of nuclear submarine, 132; of sailing vessels, 54, 58
Lenin, icebreaker, 172, *195*
Lepanto, Battle of, *138-139*
Liberty ships, 16, *195*
Lighted buoys, *160*, *169*
Lighthouses, *167-169*
Lightship, *167*
Line of position, 164; finding, *diagram* 165
Liners. *See* Cargo carriers; Ocean liners; Passenger liners
Listing. *See* Heeling
Little Juliana, steamboat, *80*
Livingston, Robert R., 77
Load line marks, *10*, 14
Loading methods and costs, 107-110
Logs: chip, 157; early, 57, 157; electric, 93
Long Beach, U.S.S., 172
Long Lines, C.S., *118-119*
Long-range navigation, 158, 166
Long ton, 14
Longitude, 153; determination of, 156-157
Longship, Viking, 56-57, *59*, 75
Loran (long-range navigation), 158, 166
Lubber's line, 163
Luff, of sail, 67
Lugsail, 56
Lurcher, lightship, *167*
Lusitania, S.S., 75, 84

M

McClintock, J. R., 126
McKay, Donald, Boston shipyard of, *30*, 60
Magellan, Ferdinand, 57, 152, 155
Magnetic compass, 57, 155-156, 158, *159*, 160; deviation of, 155-156; steering, *162;* taking bearings, 162; variation of, 155, 160, *162*
Magnetic north, 155, *162*
Mainsail, *63*, *65*, 71, *72-73*
Majestic, S.S., 81
Malabar XIII, yacht, 71, *72-73*
Maneuverability: factors in, 44; tests, *44-45*
Manhattan, tanker, 84
Manila, battle of, 128
Map-making, 153. *See also* Nautical charts
Marks, on hull: draft, *11*, 14; load line, *10*, 14
Massachusetts Institute of Technology, 36, 64
Materials, structural, 10, 13, 31, 77-79, 87, 194, 195; in deep-sea craft, 184, 186, 188; in nuclear submarine construction, 131, 134; fireproofing, 96, 100. *See also* Iron construction; Metal construction; Steel construction; Wooden hulls
Mauretania, S.S., 75, 77, 79, 82, 84, *195*
Mediterranean, evolution of southern sailship in, 54-56, *58*, *194*
Merchant marine. *See* Cargo carriers; Ocean liners; Passenger liners; Tankers
Merchant sailers: clipper, 60-*61*, *195;* down easter, 61; Egyptian, *194;* full-rigged, 58-*59*, 60-61, *70*, *194;* largest built, *70;* northern cog, 57, *59;* Roman, 54-55, *58*, 75; schooner, 62; southern (Mediterranean), 54-56, *58*, *194;* top speeds of, 61, 70, *graph* 105
Meridians of longitude, 153
Merrimack, the (renamed *Virginia*), *144-145*
Metacenter, *12-13*
Metal construction, 10, 13, 31, 77-79, 194, 195; advantages over wood, 13, 78. *See also* Iron; Steel
Methane Pioneer, 106
Micronesian navigators, 152
Mid-channel buoy, *160*
Middle Ages: geographical knowledge of, *map* 153; sailing ships of, 55-57, *194*
Midship bend, *33*
Midway, Battle of, 148
Milford Haven, port facilities, 109
Missiles, submarine. *See* Polaris missile; SUBROC
Mission Bay, U.S.S., *115*
Missouri, U.S.S., *195*
Mizzen sail, 71, *72-73*
Model-testing, 10, 31, 32-33, *34*, 39-40, *41-45*, 46, *47-51;* history of, 32-34, 77; nuclear submarine, *48-49*, 132
Monitor, U.S.S., 80, *144-145*, *195*
Mooring fees, basis of, 15
Morison, Samuel Eliot, 59, 156
Motions of ships, 37, *diagrams* 38-39; tests, *46-49*. *See also* Heave; Pitch; Roll; Surge; Sway; Yaw

N

Napoleon Bonaparte, 126
Natchez, steamboat, *195*
Natural gas transportation by tanker, 106
Nautical Almanac, *159*
Nautical charts, 153, 157, 158, *159*, *161*, *168;* of East Indies (1652), *150*
Nautical mile, 165
Nautilus, early English submarine, 127
Nautilus, Fulton's submarine, 126
Nautilus, U.S.S., 123, 131, *132*, 171
Naval Research Laboratory, 131
Naval warfare, 134, *135-149;* age of battleship, 134, *146-147;* ascendancy of aircraft carrier over battleship, 123, 148; ascendancy of nuclear submarine over surface craft, 123, 148; boarding, 59, 134, 138; bombing, *148-149;* ramming, 54, 134, 136, *137*, 138, 144; significance of nuclear propulsion, 172; 16th Century, *138-141;* submarine, 126-127, 129, 130-131, 134, 147, 148; use of cannon, 59, 134, 138, *139*, *140-145*, 147; use of torpedoes, 127, 134, 146, 148. *See also* American Revolution; Civil War; Crimean War; Warships; World War I; World War II
Navigation, 57, 151-158, *159-169;* bathymetric, 158; beginnings of, 151-153; branches of, 151; celestial, *92*, 151, 153-155, 156, *164-165;* by dead reckoning, 151, 156; electronic, 92, 93, 151, 157-158, *166-167;* inertial, 124; piloting, in coastal waters, 151, *160-163*, *168-169;* submarine, 124. *See also* Bearings, taking; Instruments, navigational
Navigational satellites, 158
Navigational tables, 164
Nelson, Lord Horatio, 134, 142
Net tonnage, 14, *diagram* 15
Neumann, Gerhard, 36
New Guinean *lakatoi*, 53, *54*
New London, Conn., 123, 133
New York harbor: cargo handling, 107-108; finger piers of, *74*, 104; ocean liners in, *74*, *100-101;* "Operation Sail" in, 53; Webb's shipyard, 60
New York University, 36
Newport News, Va., *122*, 145
Nightingale, clipper, *61*
Nile riverboats, 53, *55*, *58*, 75, *69*, *194*
Niña, the, 58-59
Nissho Maru, tanker, 194, *195*
Normandie, S.S., 87, 94
Norsemen. *See* Vikings
North, true *vs.* magnetic, 155, *162*
North and Baltic Seas, evolution of sailships in, 54, 56-57, *59*
North Star (Polaris), 153-154
Northern sailship development, 54, 56-57, *59*
Northwind, icebreaker, *120*
Nuclear aircraft carrier, 172, *195*
Nuclear engine: ascendancy of, 171-172, *195;* on nonmilitary craft, 172-173; submarine, *131*-132
Nuclear submarines, *122*, 123-124, 131-134; hull design, *132*-133; maximum depth and speed, 125; model-testing, *48-49*, 132; oxygen supply, 123; Polaris-armed, 49, *122*, 123-124, 133-134; power plant, *131*-132; safety features, 132; as tanker, 171-172
Nun buoy, *160-161*

O

O'Bannon, U.S.S., *195*
O'Casey, Sean, 9
Ocean floor: mapping of, 158, 171; mining of, 180
Ocean liners: development of, 75, 77-82; sail with auxiliary steam, 61, 77; schedule requirements, 34, 75, 103, 104; statistics, 103; steam with auxiliary sail, 61, 77, 81, *195*. *See also* Cargo carriers; Passenger liners
Oceanic, S.S., 114-115
Oceanography, 171, 178, *179-191;* study of waves, 35-37
Oil, as steamship fuel, 82, 95, 172
Oil carrier. *See* Tanker
Oil rig, 171
Omniscope, submarine, 129
Open plenum chamber, ACV, 177
Operation Conshelf, 184
"Operation Sail," 53
Operation Sea Orbit, 172
Osborn, James B., 134
Otto Hahn, N.S., 172-173
Outrigger, Ceylonese, 53, *54*
Ox-driven paddle-wheel boat, *76*

P

Pacific, warfare in, 129, 148
Paddle-wheel boats, 31, *76*, 77, *78;* replaced by screw propulsion, 78, 79-80, *81*
Papin, Denis, 76
Parachute spinnaker, *63*
Parallel rules, *159*, 163
Parallels of latitude, 153
Parsons, Sir Charles, 81-82
Passenger liners, *74*, 84, *85-101*, 103, *114-115*, *195;* air-travel competition, 100; antirolling devices, 38, 87, *88-89;* cruise trade, 100; design, 84, *85-101;* first modern, 75; schedule requirements, 34, 75; tonnage value, 14. *See also France*, S.S.; Ocean liners
Patricia Moran, tugboat, *114-115*
Payne, John, 127
Pelorus, *162*, 163
Periscope, development of, 128-129
Perry Cubmarine, 172, *181*
Persian fleet at Salamis, 136, *137*
Philip II, King of Spain, 140
Phoenicians, 136; navigation of, 154
Piccard, Auguste, 178, 190
Pierson, Willard, 36, 39
Piloting, in coastal waters, 151, *160-163*, *168-169*
Pinta, the, 58-59
Pitch, 34, 35, *diagram* 38, 39, *46-47;* controlling, 39-40, 46; defined, 37; synchronous, 46
Pitching period, 39
Plainview, H.S., 175
Planesman, submarine, 125
Plans: drafting, *20*, *32-33;* transfer to steel plates, 15, *21*, 22
Plate shop, shipyard, 20, *21-23*
Plato, 152
Plimsoll, Samuel, 14
Plimsoll (load line) marks, *10*, 14
Polaris (North Star), 153-154
Polaris-armed submarines, *122*, 123-124, 133-134; model-testing, *48-49*
Polaris missile, 123, 132, 133; computer control of, 46, 124
Polynesian navigators, 152
Port (side of ship), origin of term, 56
Port facilities, *102*, 104-105, 107-108, *109*-110; costs, 15, 107-108
Portuguese shipbuilding, Renaissance, 57-58

PICTURE CREDITS

The sources for the illustrations which appear in this book are shown below. Credits for the pictures from left to right are separated by commas, from top to bottom by dashes.

Cover—John Zimmerman

CHAPTER 1: 8—Dick Allgire. 10, 11—Drawings by James Alexander. 12, 13—Drawings by Nicholas Fasciano. 14, 15—Drawings by James Alexander. 17—John Zimmerman. 18, 19—Courtesy A.B. Götaverken, Göteborg, Sweden, John Zimmerman. 20, 21—John Zimmerman except bottom right Anthony Wolff. 22, 23—Anthony Wolff except center John Zimmerman. 24, 25—John Zimmerman. 26, 27—John Zimmerman except top left Anthony Wolff. 28, 29—John Zimmerman.

CHAPTER 2: 30—William T. Radcliffe courtesy The Mariners Museum, Newport News, Virginia. 32, 33—Courtesy The Master and Fellows of Magdalene College, Cambridge. 34—Derek Bayes courtesy The Royal Institution of Naval Architects—New York Public Library. 36 through 39—Drawings by Nicholas Fasciano. 41—Gordon Tenney. 42, 43—Gordon Tenney except top right Patricia Byrne. 44, 45—Gordon Tenney. 46—Official U.S. Navy Photo. 47 through 51—Gordon Tenney.

CHAPTER 3: 52—George Silk. 54, 55—Drawings by Cecil G. Trew from *The Story of Sail* by G.S.L. Clowes. 58, 59—Drawings by James Alexander. 61—Courtesy State Street Bank and Trust Company and Bostonian Society—courtesy The New York Historical Society. 63—Morris Rosenfeld. 64—Drawings by George V. Kelvin, drawing by George V. Kelvin. 66—Drawing by George V. Kelvin. 67—Morris Rosenfeld. 68, 69—Jack Birns, Fritz Henle from Monkmeyer Press Photos. 70, 71—Courtesy The Peabody Museum of Salem, U.S. Coast Guard. 72, 73—Lynn Pelham from Rapho-Guillumette.

CHAPTER 4: 74—Flying Camera, Inc. 76—The Bodleian Library, Oxford. 77—Courtesy Rare Book Division, New York Public Library. 78—Eddy van der Veen courtesy Conservatoire des Arts et Métiers, Paris. 79—Courtesy The New York Historical Society. 80—The Smithsonian Institution. 81—Courtesy The Science Museum, London. 83—Drawing by Raymond Ripper. 85—John Zimmerman. 86 and 91—John Zimmerman. 87 through 90—Gatefold drawing by George V. Kelvin—symbol drawings by Otto van Eersel. 92 through 97—John Zimmerman. 98, 99—Top Stan Wayman—bottom John Zimmerman. 100, 101—John Zimmerman.

CHAPTER 5: 102—Gordon Tenney. 105—Drawing by Otto van Eersel, 109—Courtesy L'Illustration, Paris. 112, 113—Top Tony Triolo; bottom Francisco Vera. 114, 115—Charles Mikolaycak, Don Uhrbrock—John Launois from Black Star. 116, 117—Joseph Fabry. 118, 119—The American Telephone and Telegraph Company. 120, 121—Official U.S. Navy Photos.

CHAPTER 6: 122—Arthur Schatz. 124—Drawings by Donald and Ann Crews. 127—Courtesy Charleston *News and Courier*—painting by Conrad Wise Chapman courtesy Confederate Museum, Richmond, Virginia. 131—Drawing by Donald and Ann Crews. 132—Drawing by James Alexander. 135—Derek Bayes. 136, 137—Photo Emile courtesy Naval Museum at Piraeus, D. A. Harissiadis courtesy Greek Navy and Air Force—Photo Emile. 138, 139—Heinz Zinram courtesy National Maritime Museum, Greenwich—David Lees courtesy Vatican Museum. 140—Courtesy Trustees of The British Museum. 141—Courtesy Trustees of The British Museum—Derek Bayes courtesy The Doughty Museum, Grimsby, Derek Bayes courtesy The Plymouth Museum. 142, 143—Derek Bayes, Heinz Zinram courtesy National Maritime Museum, Greenwich. 144, 145—Henry Groskinsky except bottom left Culver Pictures. 146, 147—Robert Lackenbach from Black Star, Derek Bayes courtesy National Maritime Museum, Greenwich. 148, 149—Henry Groskinsky.

CHAPTER 7: 150—Emmett Bright courtesy Museum of the History of Science, Florence. 152—Drawing by Donald and Ann Crews. 153—Drawings by Patricia Byrne courtesy Walter-Verlag, Olten Und Freiburg Im Breisgau, Germany. 157—Alan Clifton courtesy National Maritime Museum, Greenwich. 159—Arnold Newman. 160, 161—Ivan Massar from Black Star—map and drawings by Lowell Hess, map courtesy U.S. Department of Commerce, Coast and Geodetic Survey. 162—Drawing by Lowell Hess—Albert Fenn, drawing by Patricia Byrne—Albert Fenn. 163—Maps by Lowell Hess. 164—Map and drawings by Lowell Hess, Albert Fenn. 165—Drawing by Lowell Hess—drawing by George V. Kelvin. 166—Albert Fenn except drawing and map by Lowell Hess. 167—Drawings by Lowell Hess. 168, 169—Map by Lowell Hess—map courtesy U.S. Navy Hydrographic Office, Ivan Massar from Black Star.

CHAPTER 8: 170—Vehicle Research Corporation. 173—Drawings by Max Gschwind for FORTUNE. 174—Drawings by Nicholas Fasciano. 177—Drawings by Max Gschwind for FORTUNE. 179—Dr. Robert F. Dill. 180, 181—Elgin Ciampi except top right General Dynamics Electric Boat. 182, 183—Yomiuri Shimbun. 184—Courtesy *National Geographic* Magazine © National Geographic Society. 185—J. R. Eyerman. 186—Flip Schulke from Black Star. 187—Flip Schulke from Black Star—drawings by Matt Greene. 188, 189—General Dynamics Electric Boat—Robert Harter, drawings by Matt Greene. 190, 191—Drawings by Matt Greene, *Paris Match.* 194, 195—Drawings by James Alexander. Back cover—Drawing by Matt Greene.

A
STONEHENGE
BOOK

PRODUCTION STAFF FOR TIME INCORPORATED

John L. Hallenbeck (Vice President and Director of Production), Robert E. Foy, Caroline Ferri and Robert E. Fraser
Text photocomposed under the direction of Albert J. Dunn and Arthur J. Dunn

x